Bearded Dragons and Frilled Lizards

by
Andree Hauschild and Hubert Bosch

with the collaboration of
Paul Gassner

(dedicated to our wives Beate Hauschild and Gisela Berndt-Bosch)

Translated from the
original German by
John Hackworth

51 Colour photographs
21 Line drawings
11 Distribution maps

Matthias Schmidt Publications

Contents

Acknowledgements

We wish to express our grateful thanks to all who helped with the creation of this book whether it be the provision of information, encouragement, photographic material or specialist literature.

Particular thanks are due to Paul Gassner (Münster), who gave extensive assistance in the preparation of the book. In addition, we wish to thank the following (in alphabetical order); Tony Griffiths (Palmerston/Australia), Klaus Henle (Leipzig), Paul Horner (Darwin/Australia), Ron E. Johnstone (Perth/Australia), Markus Juschka (Düsseldorf), Bob Maillous & Dave Travis (Vista/USA). Hans-Dieter Philippen (Heinsberg), Heidrun & Uwe Röhe (Hamburg), Franz and Miklos Schiberna (Stuttgart), Nina Schneider (Duisburg), Norbert and Ursula Schuster (Rossdorf), Glenn Shea (Sydney/Australia).

The line drawings came from the pen of Markus Becker, Ginnerstrasse 6, 50181 Königshoven, Germany. The distribution maps were prepared on the computer by Milkos Schiberna, Weinsteige 18, 701800 Stuttgart, Germany who also drew the vivarium designs freehand and composed the front cover.

The following breeders were kind enough to provide us with data on the breeding of Bearded Dragons which we have presented in table form: Michael Boos (Hamburg), Maria Elflein (Memmelsdorf), Stefan Hielscher (Gaildorf), Heike Höpfl (Frankfurt), Matthias Leuffen (Düsseldorf), Herbert Lindemann (Dortmund), Robert Lipcik (Gubinek/Poland), Dieter Mouwens (Jüchen), Michael Schardt (Pohlheim), Guido Schlang (Rommerskirchen), Ursula and Norbert Schuster (Rossdorf), Thomas Stössl (Kiefersfelden), Karsten Thelen (Cologne), Wim van Tegele (Vlissingen(Netherlands), Thomas Wieske (Bünde), Felicatas and Hans-Jörg Winner (Waldkirch) - many many thanks!

Translator's acknowledgements

It was an honour to be invited to prepare an English translation of the unique book "Bearded Dragons and Frilled Lizards" by Andree Hauschild and Hubert Bosch, two of Germany's foremost and most respected herpetologists and I trust that I have done justice to their masterly text.

In this project I was, as usual, given great linguistic assistance by my friends Andrej Koralewski of Lünen and Olaf Kannchen of Hamm whilst much practical information and many helpful suggestions came from my friend the foremost Estonian herpetologist Peeter Polsdam of Pärnu, himself a gifted linguist and translator of Russian, German and English.

Biological explanations were again provided by my niece Nicola Wilkinson B. Sc. of Oxford University and Andrew Young B. Sc., also of Oxford, provided a wealth of geographical and meteorological information.

Much practical assistance was provided by my sister Margaret Hackworth and by my friends Ian Burn, Valerie McDermott and Delny Ingle who also relieved me of the arduous and time-consuming task of typing the manuscript thus releasing me to proceed with the next in this fascinating series of translations of the superb Natur und Tier-Verlag books.

Without the advice and assistance of those mentioned above, always given so willingly, often at strange hours of the night, any translation would take much longer to complete.

John Hackworth, August, 1998.
Newcastle upon Tyne, England

Front cover: *Pogona vitticeps „Sandfire"* Photo: D. Travis

Chlamydosaurus kingii Photo: U. Peters

Pogona barbata Photo: M. Schiberna

Background: *Chlamydosaurus kingii,* Photo: H.-D. Philippen

ISBN 3-931587-18-5

© 2000 Matthias Schmidt Publications
    D - An der Kleimannbrücke 39, 48157 Münster

Lectorate: Heiko Werning, Berlin
Layout: Sibylle Manthey, Berlin
Typesetting: tritec-Grafikwerkstatt, Berlin
Printed by: MKL Druck GmbH & Co. KG, Ostbevern

Introduction

For many years, Australia has held a great fascination for people interested in natural history. The rich animal kingdom there provided so many surprises that they were initially regarded as a cruel hoax. A mammal with a duck's bill could simply not be imagined. However, Australia is not only a continent of strange mammals. The herpetofauna also underwent its own unique form of development leading to the creation of such unusual forms as the frog *Rheobatnachus vitellinus* which broods its tadpoles in its stomach that has also developed as a uterus. Amongst the unusual reptiles, mention should be made of the flap-footed lizards (Pygopodidae), a family of lizards which evolved from geckos and which has no forelegs and hind legs reduced to mere flaps. These lizards live exclusively on the continent of Australia (apart from one species that has reached New Guinea).

The hot and dry weather conditions in Australia provide ideal reptile living conditions that give rise to a wealth of different species. Nowhere in the world do so many species live together as in the western Australian deserts. Despite the great interest that Australian reptiles awaken amongst hobby herpetologists and researchers worldwide, the lifestyle of many species is still relatively unknown. New species are even nowadays still being discovered and described for the first time. This is indeed true of larger species such as the very popular Bearded Dragons. On the other hand, the reptile fauna has been largely protected from many negative external influences. Australia is in no way the untouched, original and wild continent as is sometimes described in Europe. Intensive farming and forestry have altered the appearance of vast areas of natural habitat of several species so that some species are now endangered either regionally or throughout their entire distribution range.

Fortunately, Bearded Dragons and Frilled Lizards are not endangered. In the deserts and semideserts of Australia Bearded Dragons provide a very imposing sight and can often be encountered in the outback even when they are not being sought. Because of their impressive build, the fact that they are not timid even in the wild and the fact that they are very easy to breed has made them one of the most popular animals kept by hobby herpetologists. From their husbandry experience and excursions to the natural habitat of their "darlings", hobbyists have made important discoveries and have gained great knowledge of the lifestyles of a diversity of Australian reptiles, including the Bearded Dragons.

For many years, these authors have devoted themselves to keeping a variety of Australian lizards and their experience with the parasites and diseases of reptiles is clearly reflected in this book. The efforts of the authors can be commended to both beginners and experienced hobby herpetologists and will provide a wealth of valuable information on the husbandry, natural habitat and lifestyles of their charges, which will only benefit the well being of the animals.

The authors Andree Hauschild and Dr. Hubert Bosch have taken it upon themselves to write a book about Bearded Dragons and Frilled Lizards. With great care and attention, they have combined all available information with their many years experience in the keeping and breeding of these animals. They have created a book that will be of great assistance to any hobby herpetologist wishing to become involved with these interesting animals.I hope the book will be widely read and wish its readers pleasure and much success in their efforts to breed these imposing and interesting reptiles.

Dr. Klaus Henle

Preface

For many people, reptiles have a peculiar attraction which is particularly difficult to describe in words. During childhood almost everyone has had a phase of "fascination with dinosaurs" during which they were fascinated by the bizarre appearance of these prehistoric creatures. Even more recent reptiles have evolved in many grotesque forms which in some cases are reminiscent of dinosaurs - albeit in miniature form. An example is a threatening Lizard with its erect neck frill and pointed front teeth. However, a Bearded Dragon with its spiny throat fully inflated also fits this picture perfectly. It may well be that such impressive animals are predestined to awaken childhood fascination amongst adults. This manifests itself by intense interest, often bordering on the scientific and has ensured that agamas are some of the most popular of all reptiles kept in captivity. Their variable colouring, a wide behavioural repertoire, their trusting nature and attentiveness and not least the fact that they breed easily in captivity are all factors in this popularity.

Around 1979, Bearded Dragons - in particular *Pogona vitticeps* - were imported in large numbers and were frequently offered for sale. In Germany the first person to successfully breed Bearded Dragons in captivity was Rudolf WICKER who carried out much pioneering work in the Exotarium at Frankfurt Zoo. A number of private individuals also had particular success in breeding Bearded Dragons, amongst them such recognised specialists as Dieter MARTIN (Rottweil), Dieter WIMMER (Stuttgart), Elke and Helmut ZIMMERMANN (Stuttgart) and Wolfgang BRÖER (Dortmund). Later other names were added to this list including Norbert and Ursula SCHUSTER (Darmstadt-Rossdorf) and Michael BOOS (Hamburg) who were intensively involved with the less common species and had remarkable success in breeding them.

As a result of these breeding successes our interest in Australia grew. This was the land of the Bearded Dragon and the Frilled Lizard. Interested herpetologists were no longer satisfied to simply keep Australian agamas.
As hobby scientists they wanted to study the natural habitat and lifestyle of "their" lizards and to determine ambient temperatures, the animals and plants eaten in the wild and the sizes of populations, a task not easy to solve completely for a tourist with only four weeks holiday in Australia. For many years the only solution for passionate keepers of Bearded Dragons was to devour all articles published in specialist herpetological magazines and books and to exchange experiences with other enthusiasts through various organisations such as the D.G.H.T. (German Herpetological Society).

This book does not intend to denigrate such worthwhile occupations. On the contrary, it seeks - within its necessarily limited framework - to present the current state of scientific knowledge of the biology, husbandry and reproduction of Bearded Dragons and Frilled Lizards. We hope that this will make life easier for the newcomer to our hobby, protect him from the "aha" effect and ensure that all the animals are kept under the correct husbandry conditions.

Andree Hauschild and Hubert Bosch

1. Agamas

1.1 A short description of the characteristics of the family Agamidae (agamas)

Within lizard systematics the agama family belongs close to the iguana and chameleon families. They have been combined with them to form the infraorder Iguania (iguana-like lizards). According to WERMUTH (1967) there are around 290 species. MANTHEY & SCHUSTER (1999) listed 365 species in 52 genera (see appendix, Table 10, page 89).

Agamas cannot always be easily distinguished from representatives of other lizard families. Using only external features positive differentiations of agamas and iguanas is often extremely difficult. Some iguanas and agamas are so similar to one another that it is easy to think that they could belong to the same genus. If one wishes to identify an animal, the origins of which are unknown, there is only one solution: "look into the lizard's mouth". The variations in dentition, the placement of the jaws and the construction of the skull are means by which identification is possible. The dentition of agamas is called acrodontal, which means that the teeth are exactly on the upper edge of the jaw. They form a continuous row of teeth and at the base are very close to one another. Only the front teeth of agamas regrow when they are lost. Any other lost teeth leave a gap in the bite. Agamas share this characteristic with chameleons. The positioning of the teeth of iguanas is called pleurodontal. In their case the teeth are placed individually on the inside of each branch of the jaw. They regrow at regular intervals or when lost. In other respects agamas differ only gradually from iguanas in some anatomical features, e.g. dentition of the gums, degeneration of the lacrimals and by being almost unable to regenerate the tail when it is lost.

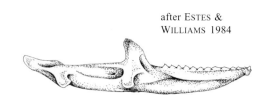

after ESTES & WILLIAMS 1984

Lower jaw of *Pogona vitticeps,* Agamidae acrodontal

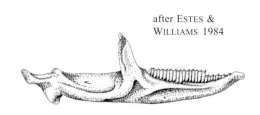

after ESTES & WILLIAMS 1984

Typical lower jaw of the family Iguanidae pleurodont

1.2 Distribution

The distribution range of agamas covers eastern and southeast Europe, Africa with the exception of Madagascar, Asia with the exception of the cold regions, the Indo-Australian Archipelago and Australia. The distribution ranges of iguanas and agamas overlap on the Fiji and Tonga islands (BÖHME 1981).

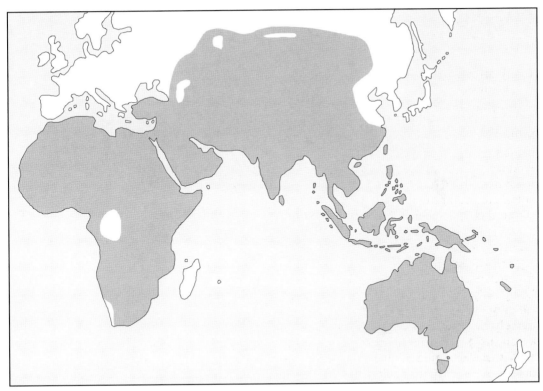

Distribution of the family Agamidae (Agamas)

2. Australian agamas

In order to be able to show the family somewhat more comprehensively we wish first of all to include the Frilled Lizard and Bearded Dragons within the entire framework of Australian agamas before going on to discuss them at greater length later.

2.1 Adaptation to the natural habitat

We gained a great deal of general information from GREER (1989). We have combined this with our personal knowledge to compile the following general section. Members of the family Agamidae inhabit all possible habitats.

In the rain forests one can find both tree- and forest agamas, on rivers and streams it is water agamas. Deaf agamas live in rocky deserts whilst others have colonised sand dunes. Agamas are found in close vicinity of the sea, in dried-out salt lakes and even on mountains. All agamas are either tree-dwellers (arboreal) or ground-dwellers (terrestrial). They are all active during the day (diurnal) and unlike some skink genera (e.g., *Scincus*) never live below the surface of the sand.

Various bodily features and other external characteristics are an indication of the specific habitat of the species in question.

Pogona mitchelli, ♂ from Broome / WA.   Photo: U. Röhe

Amongst the terrestrial agamas "sit-and-wait" hunters are distinguished by having short legs and a stout, stocky tail. Their body is flattened

Ctenophorus reticulatus, ♂   Photo: A. Hauschild

to resemble a discus. climbing and tree-dwelling agamas have a laterally flattened, streamlined body. Such animals frequently also have a long dorsal crest and a large gular (throat) flap. Active runners have a much longer tail than all other agamas. This speciality is explained by the fact that the long tail is used for balance. When the lizard is running the front part of the body is bent forwards and the raised tail provides equilibrium.

Agamas can usually run very quickly on all-fours although there are two genera which move only very slowly and deliberately, the Chameleon Agama *Chelosania brunnea* (SWITAK 1996) and the Thorny Devil *Moloch horridus*. This slow method of locomotion - even when in danger - serves not to attract the attention of a possible predator. In the wild this strategy has also been observed amongst adult specimens of *Pogona vitticeps* (HENLE, pers. comm.).

It is known of *Physignathus* and *Ctenophorus* that in open spaces they can rear the front part of the body and run on their hind legs for short distances at high speed. This is known as "bipedal locomotion" (running on two legs). *Chlamydosaurus kingii* can also run quickly on only two legs. CARPENTER & BADHAM (1970) have mentioned that *Pogona barbata* is also capable of bipedal locomotion. The senior author (Hauschild) was fortunate enough to see such bipedal locomotion of Bearded Dragons kept by SCHUSTER. Two adult males of *P. vitticeps* were taken from their vivaria and confronted with one another on the floor of a large room. Both spontaneously began to bob their heads, threaten one another and wave. One of the animals then ran away with the other in hot pursuit. Because the room was large enough to allow it both animals ran bipedally for short distances.

When sleeping these lizards either retreat into their refuge where they curl into a horseshoe shape or they sleep on a branch with the head lying on the branch and the rear legs stretched out alongside the tail.

2.2 Food spectrum

Australian agamas do not actively hunt for prey. Instead they are "sit-and-wait" hunters. This means that they sit at an observation point and wait for prey to come within striking distance. Their food spectrum includes a variety of invertebrates although some species may be particularly selective in their choice of food. An obvious contrast to other lizards is the large proportion of ants which they eat. Most lizards will not take ants as food whilst many agamas eat them in vast quantities. Indeed the Thorny Devil (*Moloch horridus*) has become a specialised feeder on these insects, although it will only eat certain species of ants. Why some species consume vast quantities of ants and others refuse them completely remains unclear. Many agamas are obviously unable to tolerate the formic acid secreted by the ants whilst the metabolic system of specialist "ant eaters" is adapted to breakdown the formic acid.

Most Australian agamas, apart from *Moloch* will also occasionally eat vegetable matter. Large, terrestrial species such as *Pogona vitticeps* and *Ctenophorus nuchalis* eat a large proportion of plant material as part of their natural diet. In captivity up to one-third of their diet should consist of green food, fruit and vegetables.

Large Bearded Dragons will also eat small vertebrates provided they are able to catch them. They will even happily consume smaller members of their own species. Larger agamas, e.g., the Reticulated Agama *Ctenophorus reticulatus* will also eat smaller Bearded Dragons as part of their normal food spectrum.

2.3 Behaviour

Members of the same species communicate mainly by means of optical signals

The social behaviour of agamas manifests itself in a multiplicity of body positions, colours and patterns. Males impress females by moving the head up and down, sometimes in rapid succession. Females indicate their disposition - acceptance or rejection - by reciprocal "head-bobbing". Males also inflate their throat and raise their body from the ground. At the same time the sides are simultaneously flattened, the back arched and one of the forelegs rapidly rotated. The latter phenomenon is often described as "waving". The greater the position of superiority a young Bearded Dragon attains, the higher it will sit (when the opportunity allows) on a rock or branch. Subordinate animals sitting at lower positions will "wave" to indicate submission and appeasement. The superior animal will bob its head in reply to this signal. This behaviour may be easily triggered by confronting animals of different size with one another. The smaller animal will cower and "wave" with one of its forelegs. In addition it will turn dark in colour. Aggressive patterns of behaviour between males of the same species and general

11

assertion or superiority displays are the best known forms of social behaviour amongst agamas.

Agamas are frequently terrestrial, i.e., they claim areas over which they reign supreme as far as other members of the same species are concerned. This is usually indicated by the optical presence of the occupant of the territory. Amongst Bearded Dragons and in particular amongst *P. barbata, P. vitticeps, P. mitchelli* and *P. nullabor* the position of superiority is usually indicated by the "spreading of the beard" and head-bobbing which can be seen from quite a distance. Whilst this is being done the beard and tip of the tail turn dark in colour, sometimes even black. If the subordinate animal does not immediately retreat the owner of the territory signals his territorial demands. If the intruder is still not impressed a conflict is inevitable and may lead to severe injuries. When excited the throat and tail-tip of females may also turn dark in colour, although not as intensely so as in males (DE VOSJOLI & MAILLOUX 1993).

From experience gained in captive husbandry it is known that the vivarium should be furnished and set-up in such a way that the animals are not in permanent eye-contact with one another. Even pure optical confrontation can stress both animals to such an extent that the subordinate may refuse food, become ill and under some circumstances die. The same effect may be caused by holding a mirror in front of a Bearded Dragon. It will not only react by bobbing its head, but will also spring towards its own reflection. In the case of *P. barbata* up to 75 different behavioural patterns have been recorded (WILSON & KNOWLES 1988). BRATSTROM (1971) made some very interesting observations on this subject and on thermoregulation. These were made on Bearded Dragons both in the wild and in captivity. He graphically illustrates many interactions, some parts of which ZIMMERMANN (1983) was able to repeat. We have frequently seen many different patterns of behaviour amongst our animals and have attempted to describe them graphically.

Graphic illustration of the various interactions of *Pogona*

Drawings by M. Becker

locomotion

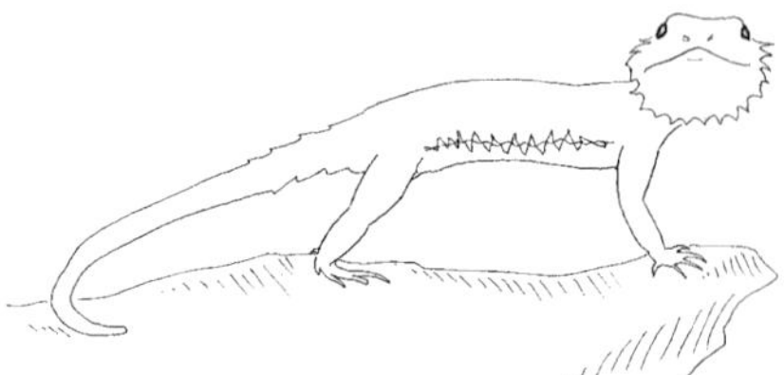

raised body

tongue test (edibility)

feeding

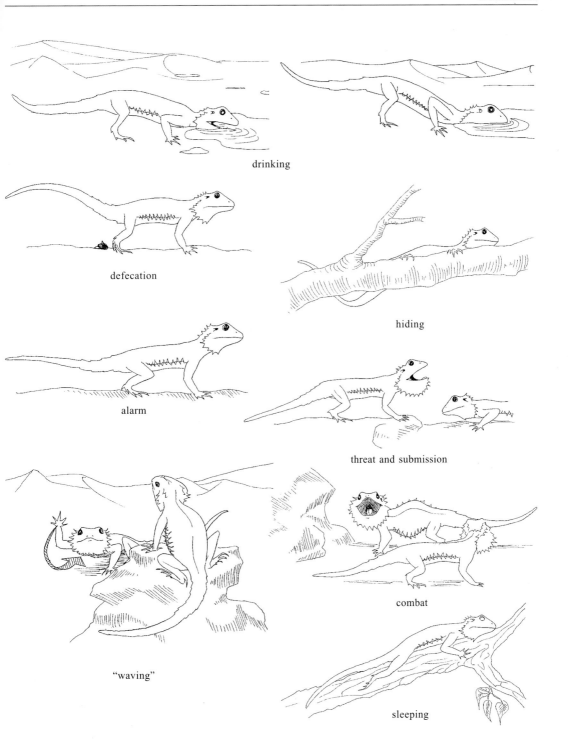

drinking

defecation

hiding

alarm

threat and submission

"waving"

combat

sleeping

13

Mating behaviour and reproduction

Practically all agamas lay eggs, i.e., they are oviparous. Animals from the dry-hot regions breed during the Australian spring and summer (September to March). The situation is different with most species from the moist-humid tropics of northern Australia. They breed from June to September, i.e., during the dry season.

Because of the cyclic reproductive biology of many agamas, mating is usually preceded by a prolonged rest period. Whilst animals in the south hide themselves away to escape from the cold weather, the large northern agamas simply undergo a rest period during the dry season. At this time they retreat into hollow tree trunks, piles of leaves, holes in the ground or rock crevices where they remain until better climatic conditions prevail. For example *Chlamydosaurus* undergoes a rest period during the dry season although other northern agamas can be easily and readily seen at this time.

The first animals to emerge from hibernation or the dry season rest period are the males. They must establish a territory before the females appear. As is the case with most lizards, agamas only mate after a more-or-less complex courtship ritual. This serves mainly to determine the species, sex and readiness to mate of any prospective partner. The main objective of the male is to apply a mating bite to the neck, shoulder flank of the female. This bite often leaves a superficial wound or at

Pogona vitticeps, a breeding pair owned by D. Wimmer.

Photo: H. Bosch

Mating and neck bite
Drawing: M. Becker

least damages the skin of the female. The male usually bites the female on the side which is turned towards his own cloacal region. This angled position prevents the male sliding from the female's back. If the female is receptive she remains still, allowing the male to bring the root of his tail into contact with her cloacal region to enable one of the hemipenes to be inserted. Unreceptive females attempt to escape from the mating bite. Under vivarium conditions we have seen an unreceptive *Pogona* female haul the male around the vivarium. She rubbed herself against the side walls in an attempt to free herself from the male. On another occasion the female was seen to attempt to reach a cave. Confronted with only a very small entrance to the cave the male finally capitulated!

If both animals are ready to mate copulation takes place very quickly and may last from around 2-3 minutes up to a maximum of 30 minutes. The male will attempt to repeat the process several times daily. Mating ceases after a maximum of around ten days. It can be easily seen when a female is gravid. She basks for prolonged periods, eats much more food and in only a few weeks has increased considerably in girth. Shortly before oviposition the eggs can be clearly seen through the skin of the belly. After 5-6 weeks the female selects a suitable place in which to lay her eggs. Before deciding she will dig several exploratory holes which are then abandoned. Eggs are laid in a hole in the substrate. Using her legs the female then fills the hole using her head to compress the substrate material covering the eggs. Finally, the hole is so well concealed that an uninformed observer has great difficulty in finding it. The female also uses her tail to smooth the surface of the substrate covering the eggs (JOHNSTON 1979). The size of the clutch depends upon the size of the female. Young females which are not fully-grown lay smaller clutches than large, fully-grown females. DE VOSJOLI & MAILLOUX (1993) have determined the largest and most stable number of eggs per clutch amongst females which were between two and four years old. Amongst Australian agamas the smallest number of eggs per clutch is two whilst the maximum may be 40 (as in the case of *Pogona vitticeps*) (GREER 1989). Most agamas lay eggs more than once each year. In this respect they differ, e.g., from monitor lizards, which lay eggs only once a year. For gravid females of tree-dwelling species, a large number of eggs would considerably hinder their movement. In their case they lay up to two eggs, often in humus-filled holes in trees or hollow branches. All female lizards deposit their eggs in a place which offers optimum incubation conditions and protects the eggs from predators. However, this is usually the end of their concern for their eggs. The eggs are left to their fate - a situation different from that with live-bearing (viviparous) species, e.g., some species of skinks (especially the North American *Eumeces* species) in which the females go to great lengths to protect their young (GASSNER & HAUSCHILD 1997). One disadvantage of viviparity is the length of time for which the female is gravid and can thus reproduce only once each year. Females of oviparous species can mate with different males and produce several clutches of eggs each year. This reflects in the number of young and the greater diversity of inherited characteristics (see HAUSCHILD & GASSNER 1995). During incubation the soft-shelled eggs increase in size by absorbing moisture from the substrate. They also continue to increase in weight until the young hatch. SMITH & SCHWANER (1981) have documented exactly the growth rate of eggs of *P. nullarbor* and were able to establish that from the day of being laid until the hatching of the young the eggs increased in volume by 83%. During the last one-tenth of the incubation period the length and breadth of the eggs decreases by 1-2 mm. These details are verified by BUSTARD (1966) for the eggs of *P. barbata* which during incubation increased in weight by up to 250%. That hatching is imminent is indicated a few days beforehand by the eggs becoming grey-blue in colour and beginning to "sweat". Soon afterwards the first slits may be seen in the egg-shell. These are cut by the egg tooth at the tip of the snout of the baby agamas which soon stick-out their head and begin to breathe. The young may remain in this position for several hours or even several days. If the eggs begin to "sweat" and then collapse without the juvenile having slit the shell it is at this point that the keeper should intervene to save the hatchling which is obviously unable to free itself from the egg. This situation can be caused by the incubation substrate being too moist.

If disturbed during hatching, the young will immediately retreat inside the egg. Once the young have finally left the egg, the umbilical cord and umbilical opening will be plainly visible for several hours. The young will immediately retreat into cover where for the first few days of life it will live from the reserves of yolk in the yolk sac. Newly hatched young Australian agamas have a SVL of 20 to 50 mm depending upon species. Adults have a SVL of 50 to 260 mm. In some species the adults are only twice as long as they were on hatching. However, there are agamas which grow to seven times the length that they were on hatching. Young are characterised by having a large head and long legs. During their growth their bodily proportions change so that the head and legs become smaller whilst the body and tail become longer.

According to information received from various breeders Bearded Dragons attain sexual maturity within the first year of life with the exception of *P. minor* which is only sexually mature at the earliest age of two years (DAVIDGE 1980).

Australian agamas have been cross-bred under scientific conditions in laboratories. *P. barbata* has been crossed with *P. vitticeps* and *P. mitchelli* with *P. minor*. The young did indeed hatch but had such badly deformed spinal columns that they lived only for a short time (BADHAM 1976). DE VOSJOLI & MAILLOUX (1993) have crossed *P. vitticeps* with *P. henrylawsoni*. The ground colour of the offspring was the same as that of *P. henrylawsoni*. The total size was an average of both species - the hybrid was very similar to *P. vitticeps*. Only recently there was a negligent cross between *P. henrylawsoni* and *P. mitchelli*. Despite having been warned an amateur herpetologist decided to house his female *P. mitchelli* with a pair of *P. henrylawsoni*. After being housed together for six weeks the female *P. mitchelli* produced four clutches of 8-12 eggs from which viable young hatched.

Thermoregulation is accomplished by various elements

Like most sun-loving reptiles, Bearded Dragons and Frilled Lizards prefer a body temperature between 28°C and 40°C during their daytime activity period (GREER 1989). They are unable to produce heat themselves. Instead they must absorb heat from other sources such as the radiation of the sun or heated asphalt on roads. In the morning when they leave their refuges they are dark, even black in colour. They move very slowly because their body temperature corresponds to that in their refuge. The animals usually go immediately to their preferred basking place. The dark colouring allows them better to absorb heat. The agamas move their ribs both forwards and outwards thus flattening their body exposing the largest possible area of skin to the sun and the ground. Once they have attained their preferred body temperature they alter their position in such a way that they are not in any danger of overheating. Only then do they leave their basking position and begin to move around to feed, defecate and indulge in social activity. Should the heat of the sun become so intense that there is a danger of overheating, they turn lighter in colour and turn-away from the sun or they move to a more reflective background. Some retreat to the semi-shade of bushes or beneath a tree. If that does not help they climb to their "raised hide", e.g., a fence-post or a tree or, should they remain on the ground, they raise their tail and legs and 'walk on the spot". Should they be unable to escape from the heat in any other way they open the mouth and pant. An overheated lizard can gradually cool itself by opening its mouth, protruding the tongue and breathing rapidly. The average body temperature of Bearded Dragons measured in the wild is around 33°C. In captivity these lizards appear to have a higher preferred temperature of around 35.7°C. The maximum body temperature shortly before death from overheating is around 44°C (GREER 1989).

At sunset the temperature falls and the agamas attempt to utilise any remaining heat. Since some objects in the surrounding area

Thermoregulation by panting   Photo: A. Hauschild

have stored sufficient heat the agamas make use of this and the last rays of the setting sun. For example, they press themselves against heated rocks. In this way they can remain active longer and better digest their food. In addition to this significant behaviour and physiological alternation, which occurs during heat regulation, agamas are also able to regulate the flow of blood in their head and body in order to regulate their body temperature. During bad weather PETERS (1986) frequently saw *P. barbata* on rocks and tree stumps. At these times the temperature was only 18°C and it was raining. There are always exceptions to general observations. Some *Pogona* species may even be active during the night provided the conditions are favourable. In New South Wales VALENTIC (1995) saw Bearded Dragons active during

Australian summer nights. He did not disturb them in their refuges. Instead he saw them actively searching for food on a road. This was at around 2035h in the evening when the moon was shining and the temperatures were 27°C and 32°C with a light breeze blowing. The temperature during the previous day had been particularly high. In all probability the agamas spent the day in cooler places and came out at night to feed. The author was able to see countless potential prey insects which were obviously carrying out their normal daytime activities during the night. HENKEL (1980) made similar observations in Queensland when he saw several *Pogona barbata* actively searching for food at dusk.

2.4 Peculiarities of the physical structure

Agamas are visual animals

Diurnal reptiles which live on the ground rely more on their eyes than they do on any of the other sensory organs, including the Jacobson's organ. They react much more readily to moving objects than they do to stationary objects. Amongst all Australian lizards families the sense of vision is sharpest in agamas. Firstly because all species are predominantly diurnal and most of their activity is carried out on open land and secondly they are able to identify prey, members of the same species or potential predators from a long distance. Thirdly, they can tell the sex of a member of the same species because in adult colouring and during part of the year there are visually recognisable sexual differences. Fourthly, most social interactions are triggered by the sense of vision. Fifthly, agamas do not rely to any great extent upon flicking their tongue in and out. Although they do have a Jacobson's organ it is barely used. This is in direct contrast to snakes and some other lizards which orientate themselves in their environment by means of this special organ in the roof of the mouth.

It has been proven that agamas are able to distinguish between various colour contrasts (GREER 1989). One feature of this is their ability to distinguish the most divergent body colours which amongst agamas serve as a secondary sexual characteristic. However, this should not lead to the assumption that agamas can explicitly recognise colours. The changes in colouring can lead to an increase in the contrast in the grey range which agamas may be able to utilise for differentiation purposes. Anyone who has attempted to stroke a Bearded Dragon will have noticed that they immediately close their eyes. This is not, as SCHMIDA (1968) erroneously assumes, a "sign of enjoyable pleasure". It is much more a defence mechanism!

The ears are less significant

The sense of hearing amongst lizards is developed to varying degrees. It is less acute than that of mammals or birds. Lower sound frequency is registered better than high frequency. Most Australian agamas have an externally visible ear opening with the exception of those of the genera *Tympanocryptis* (Greek for "hidden ear drum") and *Ctenophorus*. In both species the ear drum is well developed but lies well below the skin.

Skin, colour change and body colour

Most agamas are able to change colour for a short time. They enlarge or reduce the spaces which absorb the dark pigment in the skin cells. This alternation takes place as a result of thermoregulation or as a warning to a potential enemy. Agamas are known to undertake two types of colour change: a general lightening or darkening of the entire colour and a specific lightening and darkening of certain elements of pattern such as spots

18

flecks and stripes. They only change colour completely during heat regulation. Partial colour change takes place only during social interaction. The animals can vary their colour according to the "news" that they wish to impart. Colour and patterning also help the sexes to recognise one another.

One of the most common sexual differences in colour (colour dimorphism) in agamas is a permanent black spot or fleck on the animal's underside, usually on the throat or breast.

Many Australian agamas have a pale pink tongue and labial scales. Others have different colouring, such as for example, *Pogona barbata, P. minor, P. nullarbor* and *P. vitticeps*, the tongues and labial scales of which are deep yellow. In the case of *P. henrylawsoni* the tongue and labial scales are bright orange (WELLS & WELLINGTON 1985). The purpose of these different and very obvious, prominent colours is not yet known.

Most agamas are incapable of autonomy

One of the most noteworthy morphological features is that (almost) all agamas do not have predetermined breaking points in the tail. It is generally known that lizards can cast-off their tail (autotomy). This is a deceptive manoeuvre intended to distract the attention of a predator for a short time whilst the lizard makes its escape. Like other families, e.g., Chamaeleonidae and Varanidae, agamas are incapable of autotomy. Should part of the tail be lost the wound heals quickly but the tail does not usually regrow. Should the entire tail be lost the animal suffers by losing some of its mobility and agility. The energy loss should also not be underestimated since the tail often serves as a fat reserve. It is known that some Australian agamas (*Ctenophorus* and *Physignathus*) are capable of autotomy and are able to regenerate their tail. Some vertebrae in the central section of the tail have non-bony separation planes for autotomy. Instead of growing a new tail the Australian Water Agama *Physignathus lesueurii* grows a dark brown stump without any markings (HARDY & HARDY 1977). HEIL (Frankfurt) informs us that as juveniles his Southeast Asian Water Agamas *Physignathus cocinchinus* grew completely new tails which were totally black. Adult specimens of this species grow a stump around 6-8 cm long, the end of which is rounded. In other individuals the wound heals but the tail does not regenerate which corresponds to the present state of knowledge (see WERNING 1995).

2.5 Flight and defence

Although all agamas are capable of digging holes in which to lay their eggs only very few species make use of this ability to excavate a permanent subterranean refuge or resting place for themselves. Examples are *Ctenophorus* and *Rankinia* of which a pair will seal their tunnel from inside.

Colour-wise, agamas are usually well matched to the colour of the substrate upon which they live. For lizards this is essential for survival. Animals which live on red ground are usually red in colour. In central Western Australia HAUSCHILD and SCHUSTER found *Moloch horridus* on yellow sand and in northern Western Australia, in the vicinity of Port Headland, on red sand. The lizards were always perfectly matched in colour. Agamas which live on the trunks of trees or on tree roots are usually grey in colour whilst those which live amongst the leaves are generally green.

When attacked most agamas flee into a hole, rock crevice, hollow tree, dense vegetation or into water as is the case with the Australian Water Agama *Physignathus lesueurii*. Before fleeing some species exhibit another pattern of behaviour: they remain absolutely motionless. Those which turn into "statues" are e.g.,

Right:
Tympanocryptis lineata Photo: U. Peters

Left:
Chlamydosaurus kingii making threats from a termite mound. Photo: H.-D. Philippen

Below:
Moloch horridus, yellow (Kalgoorli / WA).
Photo: A. Hauschild

Chlamydosaurus, Moloch horridus, Pogona and *Tympanocryptis*. If this does not serve its purpose or does not deceive the aggressor the lizard will usually retreat to the opposite side of the object upon which it is sitting. Should the aggressor continue to approach the only alternative left for the lizard is flight, although there are other reactions intended to shock the aggressor. *Pogona* species open their mouth widely and spread their "beard". *Chlamydosaurus* opens its mouth widely and spreads its frill. Frequently the animals place themselves at an angle to their aggressor to appear larger than they really are. A leap forward is also occasionally effective. If an attempt is made to handle an agama it will usually bite to free itself. Only the Thorny Devil *Moloch horridus* remains completely passive. Frilled Lizards and Bearded Dragons also lash-out with their tail. It is known that *Chlamydosaurus* reinforces its threat behaviour acoustically by hissing loudly when confronted with an aggressor.

Vivarium Type I

Tree-dwelling lizards should be given a tall vivarium with ample opportunity to climb. This does not only apply to the Frilled Lizards mentioned in the text. The minimum dimensions for a vivarium for *Chlamydosaurus kingii* should be 130×100×200 cm (L×D×H). Settled animals may also be allowed the freedom of a room.

Anyone who misunderstands this warning and attempts to handle the lizard must reckon with extremely painful bites. SWITAK (1996) reports on a herpetologist who lost one-half of a finger from such a bite. It is known that when in a threat situation *Tympanocryptis* can emit a squeaking sound (GREER 1989).

22

Vivarium Type II

Smaller agames such as e. g., *Pogona henrylawsoni*, which live mainly on the ground, should nevertheless be given the opportunity to climb to a second level in the vivarium. The vivarium should therefore not be too low. We consider 100×80×60 cm (L×D×H) to be appropriate.

All drawings: M. Schiberna

2.6 Husbandry and captive breeding

Instead of giving information on the construction and furnishing of vivaria we would rather point our readers in the direction of the many books already available on the subject, especially those which were published recently. Any bookseller will order specific books (even if only for inspection). Specialist herpetological magazines also carry a wealth of information on this subject. Libraries will also (quickly) obtain books on request or are able to obtain photocopies of magazine articles. Special information regarding the husbandry and breeding of Frilled Lizards and Bearded Dragons is included in the relevant section of the "Species Accounts" To give our readers a better understanding we have limited ourselves to three types of vivaria in which the animals we discuss in the following "Species Accounts" may be housed.

Vivarium Type III

In our opinion, all other larger Bearded Dragons such as *Pogona vitticeps* should be housed in vivaria with minimum dimensions of 150×80×80 cm (L×D×H).

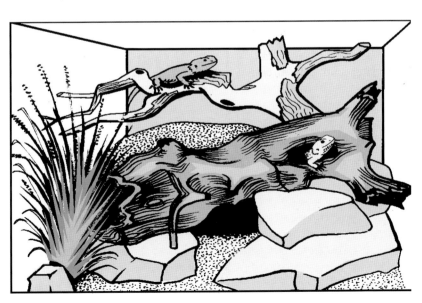

3. The genus *Pogona* Storr, 1982

3.1 General

Bearded Dragons are as popular in European vivaria as they are in their Australian homeland. They are distributed throughout the whole of Australia from the extreme north to the extreme southeast. Sprenkel (1990) stated that these lizards are also found in Tasmania but he was obviously misinformed because no Bearded Dragons are found on that

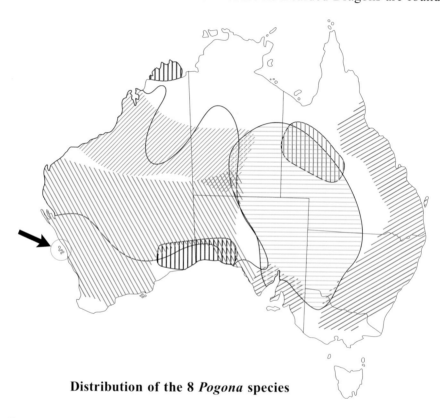

Distribution of the 8 *Pogona* species

Pogona minor		Pogona henrylawsoni	
Pogona vitticeps		Pogona nullarbor	
Pogona mitchelli		Pogona microlepidota	
Pogona barbata		Pogona minima	

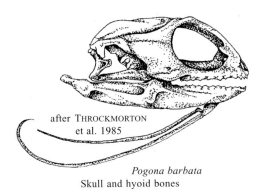

after THROCKMORTON
et al. 1985

Pogona barbata
Skull and hyoid bones

Pogona vitticeps in the middle of the road.
Photo: A. Hauschild

island. These conspicuous lizards were earlier known as a peculiar generic complex and were earlier classified as the *Amphibolorus barbatus* group (BADHAM 1976). Some fifteen years ago they were assigned their own independent genus *Pogona* STORR, 1982. The word "pogon" comes from the Greek and means "beard". "Barbatus" is Latin and means "bearded". Thus both the common and scientific names refer to the dark-coloured throat with its rough scales which when the throat is inflated are very reminiscent of a beard. Most species inflate the "beard" as a result of fear or aggression. In all probability this is intended to intimidate potential predators or rivals of the same species. Half of the *Pogona* species *(P. minor, P. minima, P. microlepidota* and *P. henrylawsoni)* are unable to erect their "beard" as impressively as the others. *Pogona* species enjoy sitting in elevated positions to survey their territory. In eastern Australia during spring one can frequently see individual specimens of the large eastern species *P. barbata* and *P. vitticeps*. They prefer habitats with loose stands of trees, frequently the eucalyptus savannahs (KÄSTLE 1973). They also sit on fenceposts, telegraph poles and termite hills. Adult males with their glossy black throat are particularly noticeable and impressive. Both species enjoy basking on asphalt roads which frequently costs them

their life. During our visit to Australia we often had to stop and get-out to chase animals from the road. They did not react in any way apart from pressing themselves even closer to the ground. When they did run-away

Pogona vitticeps with Carolin Hauschild.
Photo: A. Hauschild

it was only a few metres into the grass or undergrowth. They may be lifted and carried to safety but within only minutes will be back lying on the road. FITZGERALD (1983) saw *Pogona* drinking water in a very peculiar manner. During rainfall the animal arched its body in such a way that the water ran towards its head when it licked-up the droplets gathering at the tip of its snout. In captivity these animals will drink from a water bowl without any problems. The suspicion of ZWINNENBERG (1977a) that Bearded Dragons almost never drink is something of an exaggeration. One morning in the vicinity of Broken Hill (N.S.W.) the senior author saw *P. vitticeps* licking dewdrops from plants. On another occasion he found a large specimen drinking form a rain puddle. Bearded Dragons can no doubt survive for long periods without water. They cover their liquid requirement by eating juicy fruits and by drinking dew or rain water whenever the opportunity presents itself.

Large *Pogona* species quickly become tame and allow themselves to be handled. Although Bearded Dragons are large common lizards which are easy to catch and quickly become accustomed to a life in captivity we still have only very little knowledge of their biology. They are kept in laboratories to study their anatomy, behaviour and physiology. Many private herpetologists keep and breed Bearded Dragons successfully and regularly. However, there are practically no reports of field observations. If ever an Australian lizard species was ripe for extensive and exhaustive field study it is one of the large *Pogona* species.

Size, build and colour

The total length of the smallest species *(P. henrylawsoni)* is around 30 cm whilst that of the largest species *(P. barbata)* is around 60

Schematic representation of the spiny scales and shape of the head of the genus **Pogona**

Drawings: M. Becker

Pogona barbata

Pogona vitticeps

Pogona minor

Pogona microlepidota

Pogona mitchelli

Pogona nullarbor

Pogona minima

Pogona henrylawsoni

cm. There are known exceptions with even more extreme measurements. Bearded Dragons are thus some of the largest representatives of their family. The tail accounts for around half of the total length. The fore- and hind legs are short and powerfully built. The toes have relatively short claws. The stocky powerful body is dorsoventrally flattened. Brown and green are the dominant colours although local variants have brighter colours such as yellow, orange or red. The upper side of the body has a pattern of rhombic markings and is covered with alternating small and large scales. On the flanks there are longitudinal rows of spiny scales. The breast and belly are uniform white with an ocellated pattern. The head is broad and triangular and the neck short. On the neck and rear of the head there are spiny and granular scales. These are species-specifically formed and arranged to allow the certain differentiation of various species (BADHAM 1976). Between the eye and the ear opening there is usually a dark stripe and occasionally a triangular ear opening is plainly visible. The mucous membrane in the mouth is yellow. On each of the shoulders there is a dark fleck and an accumulation of spiny scales. The tail is not particularly long. From the root of the tail downwards there are several rows of spiny scales on the sides of the tail. On the upper side of the tail there is banding although this is not always particularly noticeable. The tail cannot be regenerated.

Sexual differences

When excited the throat ("beard") and tip of the tail can turn black in males. This is only hinted at in females. As is often the case amongst lizards, a large, broad head does not necessarily indicate that the animal is a male. Females also occasionally have a massive skull. From the third month of age the hemipenes pockets of males are already so well developed that external visual sexual determination is quite easy. We cannot recommend the technique of bending the tail to the left and right to see the hemipenes pockets as advised by SPRENKELS (1990). The sexes can be easily recognised by simply looking at the underside of the tail root. Using no force whatsoever the tip of the tail is gently curved towards the rear of the head. At the base of the tail the two swellings of the hemipenes pockets of males can be clearly seen. This is an unmistakable sign since females do not have these swellings.

Age variations

In external appearance juveniles are identical to adults, especially with regard to colour and markings. Some of their proportions are however, different: the body is smaller and the head larger. This changes as the animals grow during the first six months of life. In the case of *P. barbata* the markings on the heads of juveniles are different from those of adults. When differentiating the species the shape of the ear opening plays an important role. However, WITTEN & COVENTRY (1990) do relate how in some species the shape of the ear opening can change as the animals grow. Initially young *P. vitticeps* from the Big Desert of Victoria have a circular ear opening. Later, when the animals are adult the ear opening is oval in shape. HENLE (pers. comm.) informed us that the young of *P. vitticeps* from the east of their distribution range are considerably lighter and more contrastingly coloured than adults.

Feeding

Bearded Dragons are "sit-and-wait" hunters which will eat anything that they can overpower. As well as a variety of invertebrates they will eat a number of small vertebrates including smaller members of their own species. Frogs and young birds also from part of their food spectrum. At 50%, the proportion of plant material eaten is very high (ZWIN-NENBERG 1977b). According to season, fruit, flowers and leaves are eaten. Yellow flowers are particularly favoured. KENNERSON & COCHRANE (1981) report on a food specialist kept by them: An eleven-month-old *P. vitticeps* ate 109 dandelion flowers in a single day!

In our vivaria we provide chicory, Chinese leaves, endives, iceberg lettuce, dandelion, pieces of fruit, celery and zucchini. Canned cat food is refused although some individuals will take pieces of meat. Only very lean meat should be given and that only rarely as a supplement.

We have achieved the best results by feeding Argentinian cockroaches (*Blaptica dubia*) and locusts (*Locusta migratoria*). We can also recommend field crickets, house crickets, *Zophobas* and small snails. At San Diego Zoo SCHAFER (1979) fed her group of Bearded Dragons plant material such as papaya, peas, green beans, hibiscus and dandelion flowers. KLINGELHÖFFER (1957) saw *P. barbata* catch a newt from a 3 cm deep water bowl and subsequently eat it. JOHN (1968) fed small frogs and toads which we are totally against in principle. *P. vitticeps* kept by HENDERSON also even ate pieces of squid although these "gourmets" would not eat any of the fruit or vegetables presented to them.

Natural enemies

Bearded Dragons have always had to defend themselves against ravens, falcons, eagles, monitor lizards and snakes. With the advance of human "civilisation" foxes, feral dogs and cats and motor vehicles have been added to this list. They have no chance whatsoever against the latter! It is estimated that throughout Australia 20,000 Bearded Dragons are killed by traffic each year (WELLS,

pers. comm.). ZWINNENBERG (1977a) mentions a further predator, the "Laughing Jackass" (*Dacelo gigas*) a large kingfisher that the Australians call "Kookaburra". The same author also knew of giant snake which died as a result of eating an adult Bearded Dragon. Its throat had been so badly lacerated by the spiny scales of the agama that the snake died from internal bleeding.

Reproduction

Bearded Dragons have cyclic reproductive biology and are subject to rigid annual rhythm. The most favourable time for reproduction is during the Australian spring. Mating is preceded by complicated courtship behaviour which SULLIVAN (cited in KINGHORN 1931) and SCHMIDA (1968) describe in great detail. The male initially displays to the female by spreading his beard and bobbing his head. He then repeatedly bends his forelegs (the so-called "press-ups") and the head-bobbing becomes more intense. The female reacts by lowering the front of her body. The male then begins to spirally circle the female who responds by raising and lowering her head. The male reacts spontaneously to this invitation and approaches his partner from the side to inflict a bite to the side of the female's neck. If the bite is firm enough and the female allows it he then pushes his body over that of the female after which he slides to the side upon which the bite has been inflicted. Using his hind legs he then strokes the female's back which encourages her to raise her tail allowing the male to initiate copulation.

Males mate with several females. Eggs are laid three or four times in succession, from the end of spring into summer. In autumn when adequate ripe fruit is available the agamas then gorge themselves. At the end of this season they seek-out winter-or resting quarters where they remain until the following spring.

Gravidity and oviposition

Once fertilised females can lay not only one, but indeed several clutches or eggs each year. They are able to store live sperm. We also have this information from captive husbandry (personal observation of *P. vitticeps*). In reply to our enquiry MOUWENS of Jüchen was able to verify this for *P. mitchelli* as was SCHUSTER of Rossdorf for *P. henrylawsoni*, *P. vitticeps* and *P. minor*. At the beginning of the breeding season they only placed the male with the female on one occasion. Each female subsequently produced several clutches in succession, from each of which viable young hatched.

Females are gravid for a maximum of six weeks. The nearer the day of oviposition approaches the more clearly the eggs can be seen in the hindquarters of the female. The female's behaviour also changes at this time. She eats more greedily than usual, often stands upright with the head bent backwards and breathes with some difficulty. This is because the eggs in her belly are pressing on the breathing organs. This indicates that the eggs will soon be laid.

The first eggs are laid from the end of spring until the beginning of summer. Before laying eggs the female digs several exploratory holes in an attempt to find the ideal place for egg deposition. Over several days she investigates several positions before making a final deci-

Above:
Pogona vitticeps, ♀ digging.
Middle:
Pogona vitticeps, ♀ laying eggs.
Below:
Pogona vitticeps, a hatching still inside the egg.
All Photos: H. Bosch

sion. Females lay 8 to 35 eggs (EHMANN 1992) which are buried some 25-40 cm deep in the ground. According to SHINE (1991) females may even lay up to 40 eggs. Using both fore- and hind legs the female then carefully covers the eggs and seals the hole. Using her head she rams several layers of substrate firmly over the eggs.

Incubation and hatching

We have no information regarding conditions in the wild. According to vivarium observations incubation takes an average of 85 days. The eggs should be placed in an incubator set at 27 °C and with atmospheric humidity at least 95 %. In our own case rough grade vermiculite has proved to be a better incubation medium than perlite. We use small, transparent boxes in which the eggs are simply bedded in moist vermiculite and then placed in the incubator. The choice of incubator is immaterial, each person having a distinct preference. More detailed information can be found in KÖHLER (1997).

By absorbing moisture the soft-shelled-eggs continue to increase in size and weight until the young hatch. Some days before hatching the eggs turn grey-blue in colour and drops of moisture form on their surface. Soon afterwards the first slits can be seen in the egg shell. Liquid may be seen seeping from these fine slits. A little later the young begin to stretch and protrude their heads from the slits to begin breathing. Because this process is very tiring the young may remain in this position for several hours or indeed for several days. Once hatched we remove the young and place them in individual, ventilated plastic containers lined with clean, moist blotting paper. The juveniles are then left in peace to absorb the remains of the yolk sac. After two days we check to see if the hole in the belly is closed. The juveniles can then be transferred to larger glass or plastic containers. Our young are reared in groups of five or six in several containers. This usually does not cause any problems, especially in the case of *P. vitticeps*. However, in the case of *P. barbata* it is best to rear the young singly because they are very aggressive towards one another. Because of intraspecific aggression, WINNER of Waldkirch lost three of his newly-hatched group of six young within only a few days.

Rearing the young

For reasons of hygiene the furnishing in the rearing containers should be kept as simple as possible. We recommend the use of round-grained sand or fine aquarium gravel as substrate. The only furnishing required is a branch or piece of wood. This piece of furnishing should not have any exposed peaks. This will prevent the development of any rivalry conflicts. It is better to install a slice through a tree as a second level in the container. This will provide sufficient space for several juveniles to sit together. It is almost beyond belief how quickly supremacy conflicts can develop, and even at such a young age these conflicts can become quite bitter. A juvenile which is permanently dark in colour should be quickly housed singly. The same holds true for any animals which sit in a corner with their forelegs raised and usually with their eyes closed! These patterns of behaviour are all signs of suppression. If they are not quickly separated from the other animals they will quickly die from stress. In some cases it is sufficient to house the animal singly for only one or two weeks and to feed it well before replacing it (on trial!) in the container with the other animals. If the conflicts over the elevated place do not cease, the branch or piece of wood must be removed. In this way all of the animals are at the same level and inevitably stop fighting. Naturally, it is also important that all of the animals are approximately the same size otherwise problems will be unavoidable. This is illustrated by SPRENKEL's (1990) case in which stressed juveniles became retarded in their growth and then quickly became part of the diet of their siblings which were twice as large.

It should also be borne in mind that the animals should not be able to see into neighbouring containers. Animals which are able to see one another in vivaria standing adjacent to one another will be more-or-less obviously stressed. Although this is rarely noticed by the keeper, if the problem is not immediately resolved it will inevitably lead to the death of the weaker animal should it continue for any length of time. It is for this reason that many successful breeders of Bearded Dragons cover the sides of their glass vivaria so that adjacent animals are unable to see one another.

A spotlight installed above the basking place should allow the animals to heat themselves to around 33 °C. A shallow water bowl completes the simple furnishings. Regarding water: We have had good experiences by allowing our animals to bathe. They can be allowed to do so in a large water container inside the vivarium but it is better outside, for example in the bath (unless vetoed by your partner!). Our agamas are allowed to bathe individually in tepid water at 25°C (in which they are able to stand upright) to which a liquid vitamin preparation has been added. Initially the lizard lies motionless and apathetically in the water after which it drinks long and deeply. Only a few minutes later the scene changes to one of pure bathing pleasure: the animal dives beneath the water, turns several circles and uses its hind legs to scratch the left and right sides of its head and neck alternately. It then paddles using all fours and swims to the end of the bath with the legs lying alongside the body and waving the tail from side to side for propulsion. It is plain to see that these agamas enjoy bathing. After bathing the animal is carefully dried before being returned to its vivarium. Our excellent experience in allowing

our animals to bathe is reflected by the fact that they always slough completely. VAN STEIJN (1989) reports that his Bearded Dragons always slough without any problems when he allows them to bathe once weekly. He has never seen his animals drink from the water bowl in the vivarium - they do not need to do so because they will certainly drink during their weekly bath.

Plants are unnecessary in the rearing vivaria. Every few days we scatter some finely ground cuttlefish bone on the ground. The young enjoy picking at this. As food we offer crickets, grasshoppers, beetles, mealworms, *Zophobas*, flies, moths and caterpillars. It should be stated that only the highest quality food should be given to the juveniles. This means that any insects bought commercially should be well fed before being presented to the lizards as food. Plant material such as tomatoes, lettuce, chickweed and dandelion should also be given and all greenfood should be finely chopped. We have found that if finely chopped the lizards will eat more greenfood than they do when it is given in large pieces. Moreover, it is easier to mix the vitamin and mineral supplements (so essential for the young) with the finely chopped greenfood. Because vitamins and minerals are so important for the young, all food (both insect and plant material) should be dusted with e.g., Korvimin ZVT (available from your veterinary surgeon). Vitamin preparations must be stored in a cool place, i.e., in the refrigerator and **not** on the top of the vivarium lighting cabinet! The importance of vitamin and mineral supplements should never be underestimated because especially in young deficiency diseases such as rickets and osteoporosis can quickly occur. We do not wish to go too deeply into the significance of UV lighting here. There is no doubt that UV radiation does our charges good. Moreover, with UV lamps one attains a brightness which makes the animals very active. Finally, an old ground rule is still as valid as it ever was: as well as artifi-

Pogona vitticeps, hatchling.

Photo: A. Hauschild

Pogona vitticeps, juveniles.　　Photo: A. Hauschild

cial lighting the animals must be given as much unfiltered sunlight as possible. The tip given in standard general herpetological works of radiating the animals for five minutes twice weekly with an "Ultravitalux" lamp at a distance of 1 m is however insufficient. In our experience the distance and twice weekly application of the lamp are correct but not the five minute duration. Only after this length of time does this type of lamp attain its entire UV output spectrum, and then it is switched-off! It is much better to start with ten minutes which is gradually increased to thirty minutes. As often as is possible, during sunny weather, our young are placed outside in an open synthetic transport container. There they remain on the terrace or in the garden, under supervision, for several hours, but always with the possibility of retreating onto the shade provided by a wooden board placed obliquely over one corner. Care should naturally be taken that the temperature in the transport container cannot rise too high!

The young may be sexually mature after only six months. Although we generally keep our animals in pairs it is also possible to house one male with two or three females. The statements of KARBE et al. (1991), BECH & KADEN (1990) and JES (1987) that several male Bearded Dragons may be housed together is completely false. Of course they will tolerate one another for a short time but eventual aggression and mutual injuries are inevitable.

3.2 Species account

3.2.1 *Pogona barbata* (CUVIER, 1829)

Agama barbata CUVIER, 1829: 35
Pogona barbata STORR 1982: 201

Eastern Bearded Dragon

Description

Size: SVL: 25, TLL: 30 cm, TL: 55 cm, exceptionally 75 cm. Such an enormous specimen ("Karl") was in the collection of SCHUSTER. SWANSON (1976) also describes such a large animal.

Build: *Pogona barbata* has a slender build and has long and very prominent spiny scales of which there are four rows on each flank. The head is broad and the tympanum triangular.

Colour and markings: This Bearded Dragon is dark in colour, mostly grey with black. Melanistic specimens are not rare (JENKINS & BARTELL 1980). Along the back there is a light, rhombic pattern. Yellow flecks are visible on the flanks, toes and in the tail region. The mucous membrane in the mouth is bright yellow. Males of *Pogona barbata* present a deep black "beard". There is a dark eye-fleck between the eye and the tympanum. The young have the head and body markings typical of the species (HOUSTON 1977) which gradually disappears with increasing age. The markings on the head are three, sometimes only two, roundish grey flecks on the tip of the snout.

Differences between *P. barbata* and *P. nullarbor*: *P. barbata* grows considerably larger than *P. nullarbor* and is less conspicuously coloured. Both are found in south Australia although they do live in separate areas which do not overlap.

Distribution

P. barbata occurs in eastern Australia in a broad strip from the coast to around 150 km inland. The southernmost distribution limit is Bega, the western limit Adelaide and the

Distribution of *Pogona barbata*

northernmost location Cooktown. On the Eyre Peninsula and in the Lofty Mountains there are also two isolated populations. Thus the species has been proven to live in the federal states of Queensland, New South Wales, South Australia and Victoria with the animals being rarest in the latter state (JENKINS & BARTELL 1980).

Biotope and field observations

In Australia *Pogona barbata*, also called the Eastern Bearded Dragons by locals, is a very

adaptable species. It inhabits the tropical tree steppes as well as cool, temperate bushland and tree zones. Dry forests with eucalyptus trees, acacias, southern beech and savannahs with tall grasses are all habitats for these agamas. During the course of time they have become followers of civilisation. Because of expanding urbanisation and the increase in agriculture they are often also found on farmland. SCHIBERNA saw *P. barbata* on the trunk of a palm tree (*Livistona australis*) in a suburb of Brisbane. DALE (1973) classes this Bearded Dragon as common in the suburbs of Brisbane where it is frequently found in gardens eating dandelion and clover flowers. Because of the climate, in the northern part of their distribution range, these lizards must cope with considerable rainfall and almost constant temperatures. In the southeast it is relatively cold and rainy in the winter between June and September. Snow even falls around Sydney and in southeast Queensland. In summer it is warm during the day and cool at night. To hibernate, *P. barbata* digs a tunnel into the ground into which it seals itself from the inside (RANKIN 1977).

Reproduction in the wild

Mating takes place in spring. Gravid females are found from October to February. This means that several clutches of eggs are produced each year. A clutch may contain up to 35 eggs which the female usually lays in a hole she has dug in the ground (EHMANN

Pogona barbata   Photo: B. Mailloux and its habitat; Mallee and Triodia, 800 km west of Sydney.   Photo: U. Peters

Pogona barbata, hatchlings.   Foto: U. Peters

1992). The site is then carefully concealed. The young can hatch after only 61 days (EHMANN 1992). Other authors give an incubation period of 90 days (JENKINS & BARTELL 1980). In the Wilhelmina Zoo in Stuttgart (Germany) NEUGEBAUER (1972) found newly-hatched young of *P. barbata* after an incubation period of only 42 days. PETZOLD (1982) goes even one better by having young after only 28 days incubation.

SMITH & SCHWANER (1981) found that under artificial incubation conditions the volume of the eggs of *P. barbata* increased by 90% from the day of being laid until the day the young hatched. In South Australia *P. barbata* lays its first clutch of eggs in late October. The next clutch was seen to be laid in November/December. In comparison with *P. nullarbor* which also occurs in South Australia, hatch-

lings of *P. barbata* have a SVL larger by around 5 mm.

Captive husbandry

Vivarium Type III

A converted shelving unit (HAUSCHILD & GASSNER 1995) is ideal for housing these lizards. The basic construction is a shelving unit made from perforated, galvanised angle iron with screwed-in steel shelves. These are readily available at any D.I.Y. store. The height of the shelves may be adjusted to suit any purpose as can the length of the entire unit (by adding extra sections). Only the depth of the shelves is predetermined. This can cause slight problems because the available standard depths are 30 or 40 cm. Any greater depth is considerably more expensive. The rear and side walls can be made from lami-

Table 1 – *Pogona barbata* – The Husbandry experiences of various keepers.

	Breeder			
	WINNER	**SCHUSTER**	**STÖSSL**	**VAN TEGELE**
No. of animals	1,3	2,2	1,3	1,1
Age	7 years	1-8 years	1-5 years	3years
Food (veg.)	20%, 3xdaily	20%	20%	40%
Food (anim.)	80%, 3xdaily	80%	80%	60%
Extra UV	7 x weekly	*permanent	*permanent	*permanent
Extra UV duration	30 mins.	*permanent	*permanent	*permanent
Hibernation	6 weeks	4-8 weeks	13 weeks	6 weeks
Clutches per season	up to 6	2	up to 5	3
No. of eggs/clutch	8-25	17-25	20-32	18-25
Incubation temp. °C	28	26.4-28	27.5	30
Incub. substrate	vermiculite	vermiculite	vermiculite	vermiculite
Incubation time	60 days	63 days	67-70 days	60-70 days
Hatch rate	65%	98%	98%	85%
Food taken from	2nd day	3rd day	3rd day	3rd day
No. of young per container	up to 25	1-2	up to 30	1
Sexes separable from	3 months	1st day	8th day	2 months

*permanent means that lighting units have been installed that make extra UV radiation unnecessary. With 80W or 125W HQL lamps one achieves Uv-B values which, for example, prevent rickets.

nated chipboard or even better sheets of rigid perspex (UNVERZAGT/Duisburg, pers. comm.). These are not only very light but also easy to work with and will not rot as a result of moisture. UNVERZAGT advises that the perspex can be easily cut-to-size with a small saw or heavy-duty hobby knife. The side walls are then drilled and screwed to the angle iron from the inside. Naturally, perforated sheets should first be fitted to the rear and side walls for ventilation. The guide-track for the front sliding glass panel is fixed directly to the shelving unit and the lower edge of the shelf above using a two-component epoxy adhesive. We covered the base of each section with a sheet of thin perspex available from a roll in the D.I.Y store. This protects the shelf from scratches and rust. All joints are sealed with silicon. The electricals of the lighting and heating units are best left to a qualified electrician. Detailed information on the construction of such a unit can be found in HAUSCHILD & GASSNER (1995).

For a pair of *Pogona barbata* we suggest a vivarium with the minimum dimensions of 150 × 80 × 80 cm (L× D × H). As furnishings we use sand as substrate and large, compact branches or pieces of tree root as elevated vantage points and a large flat rock upon which the food and water bowls are placed. These animals are no longer "delicate subjects" (NEUGEBAUER 1972). Robust, captive-bred animals are now readily available throughout the year. STETTLER (1981) quotes HAAS who bred *P. barbata* whilst they were living free-range in his living room.

The husbandry experiences of various keepers of this species can be seen from the table 1.

3.2.2 *Pogona microlepidota* (GLAUERT, 1952)

Amphibolurus barbatus microlepidotus GLAUERT, 1952: 168

Amphibolurus microlepidotus BADHAM 1976: 439, fig. 4f

Pogona microlepidota STORR 1982: 211

Kimberley Bearded Dragon

"microlepidota" means approximately "minutely small scales"

Description

Size: SVL: 14 cm, TLL: 27 cm, TL: 41 cm (BADHAM 1976) or SVL: 18 cm, TLL: 21 cm, TL: 39 cm (STORR, 1982).

Build: *Pogona microlepidota* is one of the larger Bearded Dragons with a relatively narrow and short head. The body is long and flat with very small scales. On each side of the body there are three to five rows of large, spiny scales. The scales on the throat are not enlarged meaning that this species has no "beard" to spread.

Colour and markings: The ground colour is yellow-brown but from mid-body this changes to grey-brown. The rear of the head and neck are blackish-grey. The tail is grey-brown and densely banded with pale, yellow-brown transverse stripes. The underside of the body is brown and white, occasionally with grey speckling.

Differences between *P. microlepidota*, *P. barbata* and *P. minor*:

On each side the Kimberley Bearded Dragon has a few rows of enlarged spiny scales as has *P. barbata*. In the case of *P. microlepidota* this strip extends over the forelegs to the shoulder blade. This species is characterised by three to five dorsoventral rows of spiny scales whilst *P. minor* has only a single row.

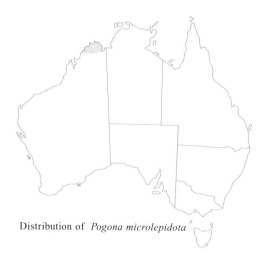

Distribution of *Pogona microlepidota*

Distribution

P. microlepidota is found in the extreme north of Western Australia in the Kimberleys. At Kalumbtu/Northern Kimberleys BADHAM (1976) found only five specimens. for determination STORR (1982) had nine animals available (Pago, Kalumbru, Mitchell Plateau, Bigge Island and Prince Regent National Park).

Biotope and field observations

In northern Western Australia the Kimberleys are part of the West Australian Plate and consist of sandstone, metamorphic quartz and granite. There is also dark basalt. In the lowlands there are layers of scree. In principle the land is very fertile but it is also much too dry. The region is an area of great contrasts; there are also tropical rain forests criss-crossed by torrential rivers. In general this is an area of untouched landscape in which the tem-

The Biotope of **Pogona microlepidota** in the Kimberleys, with baobab tree.   Photo: U. Röhe

38

perature may rise to 50 °C. The agamas are thus subjected to extreme conditions which they must overcome. Perhaps this is the reason why they are so timid and so difficult to find that EHMANN (1992) describes them as being extremely rare. COGGER (1992) states that light dry forests, spinifex grasslands and similar areas are the biotope of this species.

Reproduction in the wild
Unfortunately we have no information regarding the reproduction of this species.

Captive husbandry
No-one has yet had any experience of the captive husbandry of this species.

Pogona microlepidota, Crystal Creek / WA.
Photo: R.E. Johnstone

3.2.3 *Pogona minor* (STERNFELD, 1919)

Amphibolurus barbatus minor STERNFELD, 1919: 78
Amphibolurus minor BADHAM 1976: 436, fig. 4d
Pogona minor STORR 1982: 203
Pogona loriae WELLS & WELLINGTON, 1985: 19

Western Bearded Dragon or Small Bearded Dragon

Australian herpetologists no longer agree whether the revision by STORR (1982) of the systematics of Bearded Dragons is valid or not. According to present-day knowledge the two subspecies *P. minor* and *P. minor minima* no longer exist. Instead they are the independent species *P. minor* and *P. minima* (COGGER 1992). The classification of the last-named species is based on its exclusive occurrence on the Houtman Abrolhos complex of islands. However, not all Australian herpetologists share this opinion. WITTEN (1994a, b) differentiates between the two species by means of scale count and shape of the scales and con-

siders *Pogona minima* to be a subspecies of *Pogona minor*. In this book the authors follow STORR (1992) and consider *P. minor* and *P. minima* to be two separate species.

Description
Size: SVL: 14 cm, TLL: 26 cm, TL: 40 cm (HOUSTON 1977)
Build: This species is very similar to *P. barbata* but at the adult stage is much smaller and more slender. On each side of the body there is only one row of small, protruding spiny scales. In contrast to *P. barbata* there are no horizontal rows of spiny scales on the skin of the throat (COGGER 1992). The ear opening is triangular (BADHAM 1976) and in proportion to the TL the tail is longer than that of *P. barbata*. This agama does not have the typical "beard". The stripes on the snout are white instead of yellow.
Colour and markings: On their back these basically grey or light beige animals have a

Pogona minor, south of Perth.
Photo: H.-D. Philippen

west of the federal states of Northern Territories and South Australia.

Distribution of *Pogona minor*

pale pattern of rhombic markings. The belly is light in colour although during the breeding season that of males is black (MANTHEY & SCHUSTER 1992). The mucous membrane in the mouth is bright yellow. There is a dark stripe from the eye to the tympanum. Behind the ear opening there is always a black fleck above the shoulder joint. These animals vary in colour according to their geographic origins. In the northeast of their distribution range they are larger and more powerfully built. Their colouring has fewer grey tones and is more brown (BADHAM 1976). Should *P. minor* feel troubled it turns to dark grey but when it has basked to attain its preferred temperature it turns to a beautiful shade of yellow (BUSH et al. 1995).

Distribution

The large distribution range of *P. minor* is in Western Australia from the southern Pilbara to the Little Sandy Desert and the Gibson Desert including the islands of Barrow, Dirk Hartog and Salutation (STORR 1982). The species is absent from southwest Australia although it has been found in the south and south-

Biotope and field observations

These agamas prefer relatively warm, open bushland and woodland, in the extreme west sandy and montane deserts as well as heathland and mallee bushland. On the coast individual specimens are found amongst the sand dunes. When disturbed this agama rushes into cover. If cornered they will turn on their attacker to bite before making a renewed effort to escape (EHMANN 1992). The senior author (HAUSCHILD) and Schuster saw several specimens in eucalyptus trees along the tarred road from Mount Magnet to Yalgoo in Western Australia. We were first made aware of the presence of these animals when we discovered the body of a *P. minor* recently killed by road traffic. We checked-out the entire area and after a long search were successful. Once an agama has been spotted in the branches then one has an eye for their excellent cam-

Above: Biotope of ***Pogona minor*** in the Hamersley Ranges / WA. Photo: A. Hauschild

Below: *Pogona minor,* Alice Springs / N.T.
Photo: P. G. Horner

ouflage. The agamas all sat at a height of 1-2 metres and because of their build, colour and markings were difficult to see. When approached they pressed themselves closely against the tree trunk and remained totally motionless. Only when an attempt was made to handle them did they change their tactics and fall to the ground and run away.

SMITH (1976) watched *P. minor* on Barrow Island. The island lies 85.5 km north of Onslow in the northwestern part of Western Australia. The adult animals sat amongst the branches of *Hakea lorea* and *Acacia bivenosa*. The ground was mainly covered in clumps of *Triodia* grass.

Reproduction in the wild
These animals start breeding in spring with females producing more than four clutches of eggs each breeding season. The size of a clutch varies between two and nine eggs.

BUSH et al. (1995) describe *P. minor* from the area around Perth in Western Australia. There the females produce two clutches of eggs between October and February, each clutch containing between five and eleven eggs. BUSH (1992) published data concerning the eggs and hatchlings of *P. minor*. According to him the eggs measure 20-25 × 12-14 mm and weigh 1.85 to 2.86 g. Incubated at 25 °C the young hatch after 72-82 days. At birth the young weighed 1.7 2.9 g and had a SVL of 32-47 mm. The average incubation time known only from captive vivarium husbandry is 60 days. In the centre of Perth at the beginning of September, BROWN-COOPER (1984) saw a female lay more than five eggs in a hole some 25 cm deep which she had dug herself and which she subsequently carefully sealed and concealed. The eggs were laid on a clayey path between yarra and banksia trees. The eggs were 10-15 mm long. The

Table 2 – *Pogona minor* – The Husbandry experiences of various keepers.

	Breeder			
	BOOS	**SCHUSTER**	**HIELSCHER**	**LIPCIK**
No. of animals	4,3	1,2	2,2	1,1
Age	4-7 years	2-7 years	1 year	3-4 years
Food (veg.)	30%,	20%	20%	10%
Food (anim.)	70%,	80%	80%	90%
Extra UV	2 x weekly	permanent	sporadic	2 x weekly
Extra UV duration	15 mins.	permanent	sporadic	20 mins.
Hibernation	6 weeks	4 weeks	-	4 weeks
Clutches per season	2-3	2	3	2
Eggs per clutch	8-12	6-9	10-11	5-10
Incubation temp. °C	28	26.4-28	26-30	30
Incub. substrate	sand	vermiculite	sand/sphagnum	earth/sand
Incubation time	80 days	63 days	55-60 days	50-55 days
Hatch rate	100%	80%	100%	90%
Food taken from	4th day	3rd day	3rd day	3rd day
Young per container	up to 12	1-2	2	up to 10
Sexes separable from	3rd month	1st day	3rd month	1st month

Pogona minor   Foto: H. Bosch

fact that these agamas mate so early in the year is verified by DELL & CHAPMAN (1981). They found gravid females amongst eucalyptus bushes in mid-September.

Pogona minor is not sexually mature until the beginning of the second year of life (DAVIDGE, 1980). The author refers to the long period of growth which ends at that point. She measured and marked juveniles in the wild. Between April and September these grew from 50 mm to 80 mm. DAVIDGE (1980) also found that gravid females had a minimum SVL of 90 mm.

Captive husbandry
Vivarium Type III
Our thanks are due to Norbert SCHUSTER of Rossdorf who in 1985 was able to obtain *Pogona minor* from the area around Perth and was the first person to successfully breed these animals in captivity. It is thanks to him that nowadays we are able to obtain captive-bred animals of this species. At that time the first specimens were still classed as *Amphibolurus minimus* (also according to COGGER, 1979). STORR's revision of the Bearded Dragons followed one year later and since then

43

these animals were called *Pogona minima*. Now however, we know that these animals really are *Pogona minor*. In our opinion only Bearded Dragons from the Houtman Abrolhos are "true" specimens of *P. minor*.

Adult animals may be housed together as pairs or in groups of one male and two females. After a preceding hibernation the animals mate and produce several clutches of eggs each breeding season. The young should be reared separately. They will eat the usual variety of foods although their vegetable intake is less than other species. It should be noted that these animals have a great need and desire to sit in branches which corresponds to their natural behaviour in the wild. HOLSTER (1989) had no problems rearing the young that he obtained from SCHUSTER. His animals mated after ten months which resulted in eight young hatching three months later. These results are in direct contrast to the reproduction observations which DAVIDGE (1980) made in the wild - see previous chapter. Unfortunately nothing is known about the fate of the animals bred by HIELSCHER and equally little about the animals which TREMPE of Boerne, Texas imported into the United States (DE VOSJOLI & MAILLOUX 1993). Later the breeding of these animals stagnated somewhat and it was only in the nineties that a few specimens to renew the bloodlines were obtained. At the present time the number of young *P. minor* bred regularly in captivity in Germany is on a more stable footing.

3.2.4 *Pogona minima* (LOVERIDGE, 1933)

Amphibolurus barbatus minimus LOVERIDGE, 1933: 69
Amphibolurus minimus BADHAM 1976: 437
Pogona minor minima STORR 1982: 208

Smallest Bearded Dragon

Description

Size: SVL: 12 cm, TLL: 24 cm, TL: 36 cm (Storr, 1982)

Build: This species is small and slender and similar to *P. minor*. However, it can be easily distinguished from the latter by its longer limbs (WITTEN 1994b). In addition, on each side of the skull *P. minima* has a row of spiny scales which run down onto the neck parallel to the vertebral column (COGGER 1992). These are absent from *P. minor*. The plainly visible ear opening also allows the two species to be easily distinguished. *P. minima* has a small, round ear opening, *P. minor* a triangular ear opening (BADHAM 1976). In *P. minima* the scales on the throat are not particularly prominent which means that the "beard" cannot be spread.

Colour and markings: The upper side of the body is usually light grey-brown in colour. There is a dark, longitudinal stripe from the neck along each side of the body. These stripes enclose a rhombic pattern. The tail is lightly banded. Juveniles have a prominent black fleck on the shoulders. This feature usually fades with increasing age. The throat is either partially or completely black. The mucous membrane in the mouth is yellow. During the breeding season the belly of males is black (LOVERIDGE 1934).

Distribution

This species is found only on the Houtman Abrolhos group of islands. Amongst Australian herpetologists the taxonomic status of this species is still the subject of great debate. The fact is that the holotype originated from East Wallaby Island of the Houtman Abrolhos (STORR 1982).

Biotope and field observations

The Houtman Abrolhos originated from coral reefs. During the Australian spring (September to October) the climate is warm and mild, similar to that in the Mediterranean. At this time the temperature is around 20-26 °C during the day. The rainfall ranges from 80 mm

Distribution of *Pogona minima*

Pogona minima, a gravid ♀.

Photo: H.-D. Philippen

in September to 21 mm in November. Vegetation is sparse on the islands and is often sprayed with salt water. Bushes, shrubs and undergrowth such as *Carpobratus, Tetragonia* and *Olearia axillaris* rarely grow taller than 1 m. Fat Plants (*Scaevola crassifolia*), spinifex grass (*Spinifex longifolius*) and straw flowers (*Helipterum roseum*) have conquered the islands. Mangroves characterise a large part of the habitats of the Abrolhos (STORR 1965). As far as is known, *P. minima* is the only representative of these agamas on the Houtman Abrolhos. These small agamas utilise their climbing ability to hunt for prey amongst the vegetation. There is a rich variety of insect fauna which forms the main part of their diet. To a lesser extent they also eat greenfood and flowers. Their natural enemies are large skinks such as *Egerni kingii*, giant snakes of the genus *Morelia* as well as various sea birds and birds of prey (HAUSCHILD & GASSNER 1994).

Reproduction in the wild

No details of reproduction in the wild are available. It can only be presumed that these lizards breed in a similar way to *P. minor*.

Captive husbandry

It is highly unlikely that anyone has this insular form in a private collection. However, should that indeed be the case we would ask that the authors contact us so that their experiences of captive husbandry may be published.

45

3.2.5 *Pogona mitchelli* (BADHAM, 1976)

Amphibolurus mitchelli BADHAM, 1976: 435, fig. 4c
Pogona minor mitchelli STORR 1982: 209.

Mitchell's Bearded Dragon

The authorities who first described this species named it in honour of John Mitchell, Curator of the South Australian Museum in Adelaide. Other names given to these animals by locals are "Northwestern Dwarf Bearded Dragon" and "Pilbara Bearded Dragon". As was mentioned for the two previously discussed species *P. minor* and *P. minima*, at the present time Australian herpetologists are very divided regarding the situation with individual *Pogona* species and subspecies . We follow one of the most important publications dealing with the current situation (COGGER 1992).

Pogona mitchelli, ♂ from the Northern Highway/ Kimberleys.   Photo: U. Röhe

Description

Size: SVL: 17 cm, TLL: 23 cm, TL: 40 cm.
Build: *P. mitchelli* is a medium-sized lizard with a slender body. The head is triangular in shape with a short snout. The massive skull of adult males is particularly noticeable. The head and neck are very spiny meaning that *P. mitchelli* can display a very impressive "beard". The ear openings are elliptical in shape. The sides of the body have only one row of spiny scales. At the sides of the shoulders there are areas of large, powerful spiny scales. The legs are relatively short. The tail is long, thin and usually evenly scaled. In exceptional cases there may be a few enlarged scales shortly behind the base of the tail.
Colour and markings: This species is very variable. Its colour ranges from brown through red-brown to yellowish tones. When excited the head of males may even turn to orange or red-orange. There are barely any markings. MANTHEY & SCHUSTER (1992) describe a pattern of oval flecks on each side of the spinal column which can be seen on these animals during cooler weather.
Differences between *P. minor*, *P minima* and *P. mitchelli*: Adult specimens of *P. mitchelli* attain the greatest body weight and have the greatest SVL. The back and belly of juveniles are not so significantly marked as those of *P. minor* and *P. minima* and the markings usually fade as the animals grow. In *P. minor* the spiny head is barely noticeable and the ear opening is smaller than that of *P. mitchelli* With regard to total length, *P. minima* is the smallest of the three species. Its threat behaviour, like that of *P. minor*, differs considerably from that of *P. mitchelli* which is the only one of the three species that can display a "beard".

Distribution

The distribution range of *P. mitchelli* is in the central and southwestern Northern Territories and in northern Western Australia.

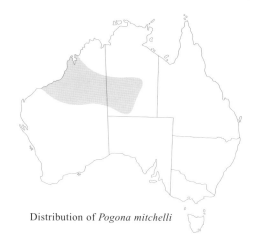

Distribution of *Pogona mitchelli*

Biotope and field observations

P. mitchelli lives in tropical dry forests, deserts and semideserts, the rocky landscape of Pilabra and in the southern Kimberleys. With the Hamersley Ranges the Pilabara region is an area of enormous iron ore reserves which are constantly being mined. Because a large area has been set-aside as a national park away from the mining industry, this rough, barren area in Western Australia provides excellent chances of survival for the flora and fauna. Deep gorges, crystal-clear lakes, untouched dry forests and endless spinifex plains provide a very diverse habitat for these agars. On the other hand, the animals must be able to survive summer temperatures of 50 °C which they do by retreating to a cool refuge. In their northern-most distribution range, the southern Kimberleys, they live for the most part in untouched landscape characterised by rocky crags, deep gorges and montane forests. Here there are also river, lakes and wide-open spaces, sparsley populated by humans and used mainly for cattle ranching. Here too the agamas spend the summer in a dry sleep. The Great Sandy Desert between Pilbara and the Kimberleys in no habitat for these agamas. Animals have only been found at the edge of the desert, e.g., HOSER (1995). West of Port Headland in the Shay Gap he found *Egernia depressa*, *Varanus acanthurus* and *Pogona mitchelli* burrowed into termite mounds. This was in January when the daytime temperature was above 40 °C.

Reproduction in the wild

In the wild the females lay several clutches of 6-12 eggs each breeding season.

Pogona mitchelli, ♀
Photo: A. Hauschild

Pogona mitchelli, ♂ from the Northern Highway/ Kimberleys.   Photo: U. Röhe
Biotope of *Pogona mitchelli,* near Port Headland.
                    Photo: A. Hauschild

Intergrades of (***Pogona mitchelli*** × ***Pogona minor***).
Photo: A. Hauschild

Captive husbandry
Vivarium Type III.
Many years of experience has shown that *P. mitchelli* is best housed singly. Groups of one male and two, or a maximum of three, females may also be housed together provided the vivarium is large enough. In captivity a female may lay up to six clutches of eggs each breeding season. This naturally leads to a considerable weakening of the female. As the number of clutches increases, the number of eggs in each clutch decreases. At the same time problems with oviposition also occur. Egg binding occurred and could only be dealt with by an operation. Breeding data may be obtained from the following table. The young can be reared without any problems. MOUWENS measured some juveniles: they had a SVL of 40 mm and a TLL of 55 mm. It is known that negligent crosses between *P. minor* and *P. mitchelli* were allowed in northern Germany. However, in the meantime hybrids have been eradicated. A photograph illustrates this "product". Nevertheless: take care when obtaining young of this species. The parents should be inspected and their "identity" checked (see also the chapter "Hybrids").

Table 3 – *Pogona mitchelli* – The Husbandry experiences of various keepers.

	Breeder	
	MOUWENS	**SCHUSTER**
No. of animals	1,1	2,3
Age	2 years	1.5-7 years
Food (veg.)	20%,	20%
Food (anim.)	80%,	80%
Extra UV	permanent	permanent
Extra UV duration	permanent	permanent
Hibernation	6 weeks	up to 10 weeks
Clutches per season	2-3	2-8
Eggs per clutch	11-16	9-16
Incubation temp. °C	28	26.4 – 28
Incub. substrate	vermiculite	vermiculite
Incubation time	65 days	65-73 days
Hatch rate	75%	95%
Food taken from	2nd day	3rd day
Young per container	2	1
Sexes separable from	10th month	1st day

3.2.6 *Pogona nullarbor* (BADHAM, 1976)

Amphibolurus nullarbor BADHAM, 1976: 440, fig. 4g

Pogona nullarbor STORR 1982: 212

Nullarbor Bearded Dragon
The name refers to the place where the animals were found, the Nullarbor Plain.

Description
Size: SVL: 14 cm, TLL: 20 cm, TL: 34 cm (EHMANN 1992), SVL: 11 cm, TLL: 19 cm, TL: 30 cm (BADHAM 1976).

Build: *P. nullarbor* is a medium-sized Bearded Dragon with a flat, thickset body, short snout and stocky tail with an overall compact impression. Along the sides there are three to seven rows of spiny scales. The spiny scales on the head are not very prominent although the "beard" may be spread but not as impressively as that of *P. barbata*. The ear opening is oval. There is a dark stripe between the tympanum and the eye.

Colour and markings: Depending upon the individual animal the ground colour (STORR 1982) may be red-brown, orange-brown or grey-brown upon which there are six or seven creamish-white transverse bands. This banding continues onto the tail where the stripes are broader and darker. On the first one-third of the tail there are enlarged, keeled scales in every third row. The ground colour of the throat and neck is light grey or white with dark, longitudinal stripes. The belly has the same markings. On their belly juveniles have

Pogona nullarbor   Photo: U. Röhe

dark-edged ocellations which fade and turn into the above-mentioned stripes as the animal increases in age.

Differences between *P. nullarbor* and *P. barbata*: both species are found in South Australia but never live sympatrically. Morphologically they are very similar. *P. nullarbor* is more brightly coloured and remains considerably smaller than *P. barbata*. For *P. nullarbor* HENDERSON (1992) gives a TL of 42 cm (which cannot be correct) although it is possible that these specimens were the result of hybridisation with *P. vitticeps*.

Distribution

P. nullarbor is found only on the Nullarbor Plain in southern Australia. Politically half of this plain belongs to Western Australia and the other half to South Australia.

Nullarbor Plain, the habitat of *Pogona nullarbor*.

Distribution of *Pogona nullarbor*

Biotope and field observations

The Nullarbor Plain consists of limestone ground covered with drought-resistant grasses and small, distorted bushes and shrubs. "Nullarbor" means "treeless". During the early middle-age of the earth, large areas were covered by the sea. During the Tertiary era large freshwater lakes took the place of the

once chalky lakes. Nowadays these are large salt flats. Such an arid area with a high evaporation rate and an annual rainfall of less than 250 mm gives the observer the impression of a typical semidesert. The vegetation consists of various bushes and herbs. Common species are *Kochia sedifolia*, *Maireana* sp., *Atriplex vesicaria*, *Triodia* sp. and *Sceroleana* sp. In the valleys of the Nullarbor there are acacia bushes. In this parched region the picture can change completely after one of the irregular, often flash-flood-like periods of rainfall. The whole area becomes green and flowers appear in a very short time. The senior author (HAUSCHILD) had a very unpleasant experience with the suddenly-appearing sea of flowers on the Nullarbor Plain on which no rain had fallen during the previous four years. The beautiful yellow flowers which he wanted to pick were very thorny and the thorns broke-off when an attempt was made to withdraw them from pricked finger. It took several weeks for the resulting inflammation to subside. The im-

Photo: A. Hauschild

The live specimen was 5 mm smaller. At the beginning of October one of the said authors found twelve eggs scattered around the vivarium. These were incubated at 28 °C in aquarium gravel. The female laid two further eggs which were preserved. the young hatched after eleven weeks. At that point the eggs had increased in colour by 83%. On average the young had a SVL of 36 mm. Their TL was 82 mm. They were identical to their mother in both colour and markings.

Captive husbandry

We are not aware of anyone outside Australia who currently keeps this species. In the eighties several herpetologists in the Ruhr area of Germany claimed that their animals were *P. nullarbor*. However, after careful examination most proved to be *P. barbata*. With a SVL of more than 50 cm they could certainly not have been Nullarbor Bearded Dragons. The six or seven creamish-white stripes along the back no doubt also confused the keepers when identifying the animals. A short time ago two private collections each contained a true male *Pogona nullabor* but every attempt to find a female failed.

pression that Bearded Dragons could exist in this hot, inhospitable region seemed impossible. However, together with my companion Norbert SCHUSTER I found one *P. nullarbor* which had been killed by traffic on the Madura-Evcla road. Every attempt to find a living specimen was fruitless. Two years later SCHUSTER searched the area a second time for *P. nullarbor* and this time was successful in catching an adult male that he was able to photograph.

Reproduction

Around 20 km east of Nullarbor Homestead in South Australia SMITH & SCHWANER (1981) found two female *P. nullarbor* amongst blue bushes (*Maireana sedifolia*). The animals were both gravid and one was collected so that ovipostion could be observed in the vivarium. The second was dissected and preserved as a specimen for the South Australian Museum in Adelaide. There were six shelled eggs in the left oviduct and eight in the right. The SVL of this female was 140 mm.

Pogona nullarbor   Photo: A. Hauschild

3.2.7 *Pogona vitticeps* (AHL, 1926)

Amphibolurus vitticeps AHL, 1926: 189
Pogona vitticeps STORR 1982: 201

Striped-Headed Bearded Dragon

Description
Size: SVL: 25 cm, TLL: 31 cm, TL: 56 cm. In the extreme west of Victoria in the Big Desert, WITTEN & COVENTRY (1990) discovered a population of *P. vitticeps* which remains smaller. With a max. SVL of 17.5 cm they are considerably smaller than animals of this species found at other locations.

Build: *P. vitticeps* is a large, powerfully-built lizard. The head is elongated and massive. The "beard" can be completely spread. The ear opening is oval. At the rear of the head there is a joined horizontal row of granular scales. Along the sides of the body there is one row of spiny scales. MANTHEY & SCHUSTER (1992) mention two rows of spiny scales. The legs are short and powerful. The tail is stockier and more evenly scaled than that of *P. barbata*. BADHAM (1976) mentions specimens of *P vitticeps* from central Australia which have no enlarged, spiny "beard scales" at the centre of the throat.

Pogona vitticeps in its natural habitat, Flinders Ranges.　　　　　Photo: H. Bosch

Colour and markings: The body is mostly grey in colour but may also be yellow, brown or rust-red. There is a rhombic pattern on the dorsal surface. On the light grey, occasionally white, belly these animals have an ocellated pattern. The blue eyelids found on one specimen of *P. vitticeps* owned by WINNER of Waldkirch are no doubt a great rarity. **Differences between *P. vitticeps* and *P. barbata***: The "beard" scales of *P. barbata* are considerably larger than those of *P vitticeps*. The granular scales at the rear of the head of *P. barbata* are in the shape of a horseshoe whilst those of *P. vitticeps* are in horizontal rows. The ear drum of the latter species is bedded deeper into the jaw musculature than of *P. barbata* (BADHAM 1976).

Pogona vitticeps with light blue eyelids.
Photo: H.-J. Winner

Distribution

P. vitticeps is found inland in all federal states of Australia up to the eastern half of South Australia and the southeast of the Northern Territories.

Distribution of *Pogona vitticeps*

Biotope and field observations

The habitat of this species can be compared with that of *P. barbata* described earlier. However, from the distribution it can be seen that *P. vitticeps* inhabits drier and warmer bio-topes. The tropical and subtropical interior of Australia has so little rainfall that practically all moisture is removed by evaporation. For this reason practically the whole of the heart of Australia is desert and steppes. The centre of the continent is thus called "the dead heart". More than one-third of the entire country is in the dry-hot zone. Sometimes it rains only every two years. In winter, between May and September, the temperature is still usually above 20 °C whilst in summer the record is over 40 °C. Savannahs with short grass and deserts with grass and bushes are the forms of vegetation in the biotope of P. vitticeps. This species is the most common of all Australian Bearded Dragons. It often sits basking in an elevated, sunny position watching-over its territory. Occasionally it changes position and goes to another branch, post or fencepost. Even during rainfall or cooler weather it remains at its vantage point but firmly pressed against the underground.

Reproduction in the wild

In Australia after having been previously mated, females lay 11-22 eggs at the beginning of October. JOHNSTON (1979) saw that females dig a tunnel at an angle of 45 degrees to the sun and some 35 cm long. At the end they dig a second chamber, again at 45 degrees and some 15 cm long. It is here that the eggs are laid after which the female seals the hole completely. JOHNSTON assumes that the bend at the end of the tunnel serves to deter egg thieves in that a thief which digs straight down will miss the eggs in the side chamber. Unfortunately this hypothesis has not yet been proven since most predators, e.g., monitor lizards have an excellent sense of smell. Provided that the laying site has not been discovered the young hatch after 89-96 days at a temperature of around 26 °C (EHMANN 1992). The same author reports on a female which excavated its eggs at the time the young were due to hatch. JOHNSTON (1979) caught two gravid female *P. vitticeps* at Whyalla, South Australia. They laid 16 and 11 eggs measuring 23-29 × 17-18 mm. The measurements of the newly-hatched young were as follows: SVL: 4 cm, TLL: 5 cm, TL: 9 cm. From these measurements one can imagine that juveniles attain a total length of 20 cm within less than three months (FELLMANN 1991).

Captive husbandry

Vivarium Type III

As already mentioned *P. barbata* and *P. vitticeps* are very similar in many respects. However, the latter species is slightly more suitable for captive husbandry and the

Table 4 – *Pogona vitticeps* – The Husbandry experiences of various keepers.

	Breeder					
	WINNER	**ELFLEIN**	**THELEN**	**HÖPFL**	**LINDEMANN**	**WIESKE**
No. of animals	1,4	1,1	1,1	1,2	1,1	1,1
Age	up to 7 years	4 years	1,5 years	2 years	3 years	8 years
Food (veg.)	50%, 3 x daily	20%	40%	40%	30%	25%
Food (anim.)	50%, 3 x daily	80%	60%	60%	70%	75%
Extra UV	daily	3 x weekly	2 x weekly	permanent	1 x weekly	3 x weekly
Extra UV duration	30 mins.	10 mins	10 mins	permanent	5 mins.	15 mins.
Hibernation	10 weeks	-,-	8 weeks	9 weeks	6 weeks	7 weeks
Clutches per season	up to 6	1	2	3	2	3
Eggs per clutch	8-25	25	11-21	10-16	20-21	13-16
Incubation temp. °C	28	28	29	27	28	27
Incub. substrate	vermiculite	vermic/sand	sand/seramis	vermiculite	pott. comp/sand	vermiculite
Incubation time	2 months	71-78 days	58 days	72-84 days	66-80 days	84-116 days
Hatch rate	50%	94%	50%	84%	67%	75%
Food taken from	2nd day	2nd day	3rd day	2nd day	6th day	5th day
Young per container	up to 25	up to 20	5-6	6-8	14	10
Sexes separable from	3rd month	4th week	sold	sold	sold	8th week

young may be reared in groups. The vivarium conditions should be as described earlier.

After their first hibernation the males establish a system of superiority which is maintained throughout the year. To prevent any unpleasant occurrences the weaker animals should be separated. Although it is possible to house a group of one male and two or three females together we advise that the animals be housed singly or in pairs.

HENDERSON (1992) reared young that were sexually mature after only ten months. In the eleventh month of its life a female laid a clutch of 24 eggs. Good and detailed information regarding the breeding of *P. vitticeps* may be obtained from the article cited above although the animals pictured is *P. vitticeps* and not *P. barbata* which detracts somewhat from the good total impression of this work.

Pogona vitticeps, a portrait, Whyalla / SA.
Photo: A. Hauschild

Table 4a – *Pogona vitticeps* – The Husbandry experiences of various keepers.

	Breeder					
	SCHARDT	**LEUFFEN**	**HAUSCHILD**	**IMHOF**	**SCHUSTER**	**BOOS**
No. of animals	1,2	1,2	1,1	2,2	3,6	3,7
Age	4 years	2 years	3 years	3-4 years	1-11 years	3-8 years
Food (veg.)	50%	60%	30%	20%	30%	30%
Food (anim.)	50%	40%	70%	80%	70%	70%
Extra UV	3 x weekly	1 x weekly	permanent	2 x weekly	permanent	1-2 x weekly
Extra UV duration	15 mins.	5 mins	permanent	5 mins.	permanent	15 mins.
Hibernation	7 weeks	8 weeks	8-12 weeks	8 weeks	up to 12 weeks	9-12 weeks
Clutches per season	2	3	3	3	2 per female	3-6
Eggs per clutch	15-19	22-24	14-22	15-22	15-26	22-30
Incubation temp. °C	28-30	28	31	26	26.4-28	27-20
Incub. substrate	vermiculite	vermiculite	vermiculite	vermiculite	vermiculite	sand
Incubation time	63-75 days	65-75 days	60 days	56 days	63 days	approx. 80 days
Hatch rate	100%	98%	95%	50%	98%	98%
Food taken from	5th day	3rd day	4th day	4th day	3rd day	4th day
Young per container	5	4	3	up to 22	2-5	10-15
Sexes separable from	-,-	2nd week	3rd month	15 cm TL	1st day	20 cm TL

3.2.8 *Pogona henrylawsoni* WELLS & WELLINGTON, 1985

Pogona brevis WITTEN, 1994: 331
Pogona henrylawsoni WELLS & WELLINGTON, 1985

Lawson's Bearded Dragon, Dwarf Bearded Dragon, Black Earth Bearded Dragon.

Comments to the name of the species

P. henrylawsoni was only described in 1985 as the eighth of the seven species previously described by WELLS & WELLINGTON (1985). The work was not limited to new descriptions. Instead it compiled a list of all amphibians and reptiles of Australia and was a way or reckoning with the strictly conservative nomenclature system. The authors partially took-over some archaic names, but also allocated arbitrary names after words they had created themselves or which originated in comics and science fiction. Their work, "A Classification of the Amphibia and Reptilia of Australia" was outlawed by international science. To quote one example: From the skink genus *Pseudemoia* (FUHN 1967) the two authors excluded the species *P. lichenigera* and proclaimed the new genus *Vaderscincus gen. nov.* They named the new genus after Darth Vader, a character from the film "Star Wars". Although this work is not contained in its index despite an application from Australian herpetologists to the Zoological Nomenclature Commission, Australian herpetologists are still very divided on the subject.

The truth of the matter is however, that the holotype of the Bearded Dragon was found in 1978 by G. HUSBAND and J. SAUER 118 km west of Richmond in Queensland. The description of *P. henrylawsoni* by WELLS & WELLINGTON originated in 1982. In the meantime, around 1982, some gravid females of this species had reached Europe and several arrived in Germany. At that time they had no scientific name. All that was known was that they must be agamas belonging to the *Amphibolurus* complex. From whence should a name be derived? These agamas were not difficult to breed and because so many young were being captive-bred they had to be given a serious name. It was not possible to publish the first description in Germany because although the animals were indeed present there, the exact location of where they had been found was not known. A first description was also not possible in Australia because officially Australians knew nothing about the existence of this species until 1985. To all appearances they conducted enquiries but remained unsuccessful until WELLS & WELLINGTON's 1995 publication. Naturally, Australian herpetologists were aware that a new, and as yet undescribed species of Bearded Dragon was being smuggled to Europe. Because of the apathy of some Australian herpetologists only to publish long after new discoveries had been made (HENLE 1993), the species still remained undescribed. It is therefore no wonder that amateur herpetologists fascinated with Australian reptiles should stumble upon WELLS & WELLINGTON's 1983 work when searching for reference literature. These authors listed all seven known species of *Pogona* followed immediately by *Rankinia* gen. nov. Thus begins the new description of a new genus, namely that of the separated *Tympanocryptis adelaidensis*, *T. chapmani* and *T. diemensis*. WELLS & WELLINGTON (1983) had chosen the name *Rankinia* in memory of the accidentally killed amateur herpetologist Peter Robert RANKIN. However, using the name *Rankinia* in no way did they mean a new name for the species, especially not one of the *Pogona* complex. The work of

WELLS & WELLINGTON (1983) is a flowing text without subdivision into paragraphs. Therefore a superficial reader would think that he had seen a description of an eighth *Pogona* species, namely *Pogona (Amphibolurus) raninii*.

It was in this unorthodox way that German amateur herpetologists came upon the "name of species" of a previously undescribed *Pogona*. What a disappointment when the new 1986 edition of COGGER's "Bible" contained not one word about *Pogona rankinii*. To date nothing has changed. WITTEN made use of the report of the loss of the holotype to give a new description of this agama: WELLS had borrowed the holotype from the museum because he wished to submit an exact description of *P. henrylawsoni*. Unfortunately however, the museum specimen was lost. Once this news was made public then WITTEN set-out to find further specimens from which he could provide a new description. After searching for several months he found three specimens which he used to describe *P. brevis*. In this way, in 1994 (WITTEN 1994a) he described *P. henrylawsoni* as *P. brevis*. He chose the name "*brevis*" because the head, body, tail and legs of this species are very stocky. SHEA (1995) contested the new description of *P. brevis* on the grounds of inaccuracies in WITTEN's work in the species name *henrylawsoni*. Because both names referred to the same species *P. henrylawsoni* had to take precedence.

Description

Size: SVL: 13 cm, TLL: 17 cm, TL: 30 cm.
Build: *P. henrylawsoni* is the smallest of the eight Bearded Dragons with a compact body and short, powerful limbs. The head is roundish and not triangular like that of most other Bearded Dragons. The "beard" and spiny scales on the head are only poorly developed. There is a row of spiny scales along each side of the body. In comparison with other mem-

Pogona henrylawsoni, gravid ♀♀.
Photo: A. Hauschild

bers of the genus the tail of this agama is the shortest.

Colour and markings: The ground colour is variable, sometimes light grey, sometimes orange-brown. the throat has irregular striping. The bright orange mucous membrane in the mouth presents a great contrast. The dorsal markings are also variable and on some specimens may take the form of angular or oval grey flecks whilst on others it is washed-out and almost unrecognisable. Beneath the ear opening there is often an orange-red fleck, frequently covered by a fold skin.

Distribution

Central and northwestern Queensland. The few known locations are Richmond (where the holotype was found), Hughenden, Mittaburra, Longreach and Aramac.

Distribution of *Pogona henrylawsoni*

Biotope and field observations

P. henrylawsoni lives on the so-called black earth ground (the ground of the semi-humid zone). This transition zone to the semi-desert is characterised by relatively high rainfall 8400-800 mm) concentrated mainly to the summer months. Because of the high content of montmorrillonitic clay minerals black ground earth tends to form dry clefts and small formations which in Australia are known as "gilgais". Black ground is relatively fertile and is generally used for meadows although it is also good for the cultivation of wheat and barley (LÖFFLER & GROTZ 1995). This means that because of agriculture the occurrence of this agama is somewhat limited within its distribution range. The top layer of black earth is interspaced with rocks and covered with tufts of grass (known as Mitchell Grass in Australia). There are almost no trees in this vegetation zone (HORNER, pers. comm.). This description of the biotope corresponds with that given by EHMANN (1992) who limits the distribution range of this species to an area of some 200,000 km². he states that the population density is low but "probably secure". There is barely any more ecological data con-

Pogona henrylawsoni and its biotope in the black soil country. Photos: P. Horner

cerning *P. henrylawsoni* in any available her petological literature.

The local inhabitants of central Queensland call the location where *P. henrylawsoni* is found "downs country". WITTEN (1994a found two specimens on an unsurfaced track

Within the distribution range this was the sum total of animals found during the several months he had allocated for the study of this region. He comes to the conclusion that *P. henrylawsoni* has completely different territorial behaviour to all other *Pogona* species which always sit at an elevated vantage point. By sheer coincidence SHEA & SADLER identified one of the natural predators on *P. henrylawsoni*. A newly-caught venomous snake *Pseudechis colletti* regurgitated its last meal, namely a *P. henrylawsoni* (SHEA 1995).

In this connection it is interesting to note that the distribution range of the snake is also the distribution range of this Bearded Dragon.

Reproduction in the wild
Reproduction data from the wild is not available. Eggs were found in two museum specimens. One specimen (SVL 12 cm) contained five eggs in its oviduct and the other (SVL 11 cm) nine eggs.

Captive husbandry
Pogona henrylawsoni, locally affectionately called "Mini Cooper" because of its stocky build (MARTIN/Rottweil) is the most popular Bearded Dragon amongst hobby herpetologists. Because it is easy to keep and breed and only requires a relatively small ground area its place in hobby herpetology has been guaranteed. It is not only lizard enthusiasts who keep these animals. Many fans of snakes, frogs, tortoises and turtles also have

an additional vivarium housing a small group of *P. henrylawsoni*. These animals may be kept under the "usual Bearded Dragon" conditions described earlier. DE VOSJOLI (1996) for example, describes how a very attractive vivarium can be created for this species. The species is easy to handle, is not timid and is not at all selective in its choice of food. I can tolerate a wide temperature range and can usually be seen throughout the day. I should be given a two-month hibernation a room temperature and with the lighting switched-off, after which, at most two or three weeks later, the first matings will be seen. Eggs follow after a further four weeks A clutch may contain between five and 18 eggs. Up to five clutches of eggs have been laid in one breeding season. Newly-laid eggs are oval in shape, approximately 2 cm long and 1 cm wide. As the eggs develop they become more spherical in shape. They should be incubated at 28 °C. The young hatch af

Table 5 – *Pogona henrylawsoni* – The Husbandry experiences of various keepers.

	Breeder				
	MOUWENS	**HÖPFL**	**SCHLANG**	**SCHUSTER**	**HAUSCHILD**
No. of animals	1,1	1,5	1,2	1,2	1,1
Age	3 years	3 years	5 years	2 years	4 years
Food (veg.)	5%,	20%	30%	30%	35%
Food (anim.)	95%,	80%	70%	70%	65%
Extra UV	1 x weekly	permanent	2 x weekly	permanent	2 x weekly
Extra UV duration	10 mins.	permanent	20 mins.	permanent	30 mins.
Hibernation	8 weeks	6 weeks	6 weeks	4-12 weeks	5 weeks
Clutches per season	4	2	3-4	3	3-4
Eggs per clutch	15-21	11-18	9-20	13-17	12-18
Incubation temp. °C	28	28	29	26.4-28	30
Incub. substrate	vermiculite	vermiculite	vermiculite	vermiculite	vermiculite
Incubation time	55 days	59-71 days	50-60 days	56-64 days	50-65 days
Hatch rate	95%	90%	99%	95%	95%
Food taken from	2nd day	3rd day	3rd day	3rd day	3rd day
Young per container	5	6-8	5-10	2-3	3
Sexes separable from	2nd week	-,-	-,-	3rd day	2nd month

ter around ten weeks and have the following measurements: SVL 40 mm, TLL 40 mm, TL 80 mm. Although they have so much in their favour, there is also something negative to report. In some breeding lines some genetic defects have been reported giving rise to deformed specimens of *P. henrylawsoni*. Young with curled or kinked tails, deformed spinals columns and overgrown organs are not rare. These should be immediately euthanased and the relevant parents no longer used for breeding purposes. These deformations cannot always be traced back to the underprovision of supplements to the parents but are much more usually a genetic defect in at least one of the breeding animals. Unfortunately, we have recently been hearing about the high mortality rate of juvenile *P. henrylawsoni*. On the one hand viral infections may be the cause, but it is also thought that food insects bought commercially may be responsible. Only a few hours after being fed on the most minute commercially available crickets the young have been known to die from fits and cramp. However, most breeders supply healthy animals although it is impor-

Pogona henrylawsoni, a captive-bred juvenile.
Photo: A. Hauschild

tant when purchasing captive-bred young to also inspect the parents to ensure that they are well housed and taken care of and that they also appear healthy. Only then will the prospective purchaser be able to feel confident that healthy, viable young have been bought. The life expectancy of *P. henrylawsoni* is around fifteen years.

3.3 Colour breeding

In the United States several people have been deliberately breeding certain colour morphs of Bearded Dragons for some time. The species chosen for this was *Pogona vitticeps* which is the most commonly kept species. The colour range contains several extreme colours which would never be found amongst wild-caught Australian animals. As a basis for such a breeding programme one nevertheless requires naturally coloured animals, some of which are naturally a reddish or yellowish colour. In central Australia *Pogona vitticeps* is perfectly matched in colour to the red sandy ground of the outback. The yellow colouring is an adaptation by these animals to the colour of the sandy ground in

their southern distribution range. It is not the job of the present authors to attempt to persuade American breeders to stop producing their colour creations. It is "only" a matter of specimens being produced in captivity to meet the demands of certain fashion trends in captive herpetological circles. We wish to extend our thanks to Robert MAILLOUX for making slides of these unusually coloured animals available to us.

Whether these specially-bred colour forms are limited in their ability to communicate and thermoregulate or whether their social behaviour has been altered is beyond our knowledge. If they are to be kept in outdoor enclosures there arises the question of

Pogona vitticeps
"Sandfire-Red-Gold"
Photo: D. Travis

Pogona vitticeps
"Sandfire-Gold"
Photo: D. Travis

Pogona vitticeps
"Sandfire-Yellow"
Photo: D. Travis

Pogona vitticeps
"Pastels"
Photo: D. Travis

Pogona vitticeps "Sandfire".   Photo: D. Travis

whether animals with reduced pigment are more sensitive to UV radiation.

The American colour morphs are:
a) "Sandfire" TM Dragon. Head and legs are carmine red whilst the dorsal surface is less red in colour. There are no markings or patterning. The breeder Robert MAILLOUX, owner of the Sandfire Dragon Ranch from Vista, California has registered this colour variant as a trade mark (TM = Trade Mark).
b) "Red Gold Dragon". The head is either deep red, orange or yellow. The body and legs are grey or yellow.
c) "Red Dragon". These agamas have a red head and are red on each side of the spinal column. The typical rhombic pattern on the back is also very dark.
d) "Yellow Dragon". The head is pale yellow to bright yellow. The body has various shades of yellow.
e) "Pastel Dragon". The loss of the dark pigment is being more and more inbred.

3.4 Hybrid Bearded Dragons

"Vittikins" is **the** current American artificial product. The great hit! Finally, a "large Bear-ded Dragon which only grows to a medium size". A female *P. henrylawsoni* and a male *P. vitticeps* have allowed the American breeder RYBAK to produce a creation which she offers for sale as "Vittikin". The advantages: A medium-sized Bearded Dragon that has the temperament of a large one but which eats only around half as much and is hand-tame. The offspring of "Vittikins" are not sterile. They breed without any problems, producing three clutches of eggs each year, each clutch containing an average of up to 17 eggs. The breeder of these animals excuses herself for their wide distribution in the captive herpetology circle with the statement that the product should be recognised as such and nothing else. Moreover in herpetologist publicity material (RYBAK 1996) she states that some of the offspring resemble *P. vitticeps* very closely whilst the remainder are similar to *P. henrylawsoni*. It is therefore obvious that the introduction of these crosses into pure-bred colonies is inevitable and pre-programmed. Members of various species do not interbreed under natural circumstances since they are reproductively isolated from one another by a multitude of mechanisms, e.g., they live in different biotopes, have different activity periods or are geographically separated. However, this does not rule-out fertile hybridisation in captivity, as has been the case in this instance. In addition one cannot rule-out the possibility that the hybrids - as attractive as they are - may be carriers of genetic defects which manifest themselves in an increased number of deformed young or a total collapse of the population.

Every serious breeder should therefore strive to ensure that only animals of the same species are allowed to mate. Only in that way can it be ensured that the species remains a taxonomic unit. Hybrids are indeed useful for scientific purposes but it is important that such cross-breeding is carried-out under controlled conditions.

4. The genus *Chlamydosaurus* GRAY, 1825

4.1 General

"Chlamys" comes from the Greek language and means "cape" or "cloak". The species name refers to Philip King Parker (1791-1856) an admiral in the British navy (STORR et al. 1983). *Chlamydosaurus* is a monotypic genus. For many years the question has been asked whether there is really only one species of Frilled Lizard. Are the significantly differently coloured and marked populations of Indonesia not an entirely different species? Whether a thorough examination of the status of these lizards would result in three species or two species is uncertain but both variants are possible.

4.2 Species account

4.2.1 *Chlamydosaurus kingii* GRAY, 1825

Frilled Lizard

Description

Size: SVL: 28cm, TLL: 67cm, TL: 95cm. PETERS (1986) knows of a specimen with a TL of more than 1 metre!

Build, colour and markings: the body is somewhat flattened on the sides and is covered with small scales. There is a small gular crest of slightly enlarged scales. The long, whip-like tail accounts for two-thirds of the total length. The forelegs are short and the hind legs much longer (HARCOURT 1986). The frill is comprised of an enormous fold of skin which is supported by cartilaginous extensions of the hyoid bone. The snout is horny and hard. There are no movable tissue structures on the outside of the mouth. Because this lizard does not have movable lips it has to draw food into its mouth by movements of the upper and lower jaws. It does not use its forelegs in this process. The tongue, a broad, fleshy organ on the base of the mouth, is rounded. Beneath the tongue there are scaly plates which protect the tongue from the lower, pointed front teeth. The surface of the tongue is covered with nodules, some of which contain taste buds. The tongue may be protruded slightly forwards and is thus mobile so that it can move bulky food around in the mouth. The tongue also transmits taste particles to the Jacobson's organ which "assists" the sense of smell. The tongue is equipped with a series of bones and cartilages which support it and which as a whole form the hyoid skeleton. This is connected to the edges of the lower jaw by various muscles as is its rear to the breastbone. On the one hand it supports the throat tissue when eating, drinking and breathing and on the other it causes the erection of the frill. Furthermore, the hyoid skeleton servers as the connection point for muscles which are responsible for protruding and withdrawing the tongue.

Chlamydosaurus kingii, ♂
Photo: H. Bosch

f the animal is startled it opens its mouth and flexes the muscles running from the hyoid bone and through the neck frill like the spokes of an umbrella. The neck frill is thus also vertically raised and presents the small head in a very large fan. It encloses the entire skull on both sides and below to such an extent that only the forelegs of the animal are visible. The remainder is hidden behind the large neck frill. The large, pointed front teeth act in the same way as the incisors of a beast of prey. Loud hissing and the lashing of the whip-like tail complete the picture of a lizard which is very well able to put-up a vigorous fight. Under normal circumstances the frill lies in folds alongside the body. During mating the frill is also erected and shown in all its glory. Only when fully erected can the beautiful colours and markings of the frill be seen: red, yellow, black and white, all in great contrast to the yellow-brown body. At one time it was thought that the frill was erected to serve as a sound reflector to enable these animals to hear better. However, it is now known that this is not the case (WERMUTH 1959). In their book, under the heading **"Umbrella trick"** BURTON & BURTON (1976) give two examples which we wish to quote here: "History does not record whether any of the learned zoologists noticed a comparison between the lizard and a lady. At that time ladies carried parasols and it was not uncommon for a lady, confronted by a cow as she crossed a field, to frighten the cow away by suddenly opening her parasol in its face. Konrad Lorenz, in King Salomon's Ring, tells how his wife kept geese from devastating her newly-planted flower beds. She carried a large scarlet umbrella and this she would suddenly unfold at the geese with a jerk, causing the geese to take to the air with a thundering of wings. It is almost instinctive for a woman carrying an umbrella to use it in this way against a powerful and persistent opponent. It is a matter of no small

Chlamydosaurus kingii, ♀   Photo: H. Bosch

interest to find that this same effective defence should have been evolved by lizard."

Sexual differences

The sexes of *C. kingii* are best distinguished whilst the animals are still young. REISINGER (1995) states that careful attention should be given to the root of the tail. Before these animals are three months old males may be recognised by their prominent hemipenes pockets. Later this is not possible because the tail joint becomes so thick that the hemipenes pockets can no longer be seen as such. In general, males grow larger than females. An adult may weigh up to 900g. Females weigh considerably less. For a female with a SVL of 24 cm SHINE (1990) gives a weight of 400g.

Age variations and life expectancy
Juveniles are identical to adults in appearance although the frill is smaller and less well developed (COGGER 1992). They begin to show territorial behaviour from around four months of age. SPRACKLAND (1993) suspects that *C. kingii* has a life expectancy of between five and seven years. REISINGER (pers. comm.) is currently breeding from an eight-year-old female and guesses that some individuals of this species may live considerably longer than ten years.

Distribution
Chlamydosaurus kingii is found in three federal states in northern Australia and in southern New Guinea.

Distribution of *Chlamydosaurus kingii*

The Australian animals differ in both colour and markings from those in New Guinea. The populations found in Queensland also differ in colour from those found in the Northern Territories. The brightest colours are found on animals from the north and northwest. The Queensland populations tend more to a sombre brown or grey (HOSER 1989). The populations in the Northern Territories are larger than those in Queensland.
The following descriptions refers to Australian Frilled Lizards.

Biotope
The diurnal Frilled Lizard lives on open bushland, in open forests and on grassland. Ninety percent of their life is spent in elevated places such as trees and bushes (SHINE & LAMBECK 1989). They do not have a regular resting place. They can be found anywhere: on the ground, on fenceposts, on fallen trees or termite hills. When they are alarmed they press themselves against the underground. When these animals are on bark their colours are particularly well matched. Alternatively, when disturbed they run quickly to the other side of the tree so that a prospective aggressor can no longer see them. Should they decide to flee they descend from the tree, but not head-first. Instead they slide down backwards. It is only when they are near the bottom of the tree that they turn and leap head-first to the ground and flee-away at great speed running only on the hind legs. The forelegs are held alongside the body. When running in this way the tail is held horizontal and assumes a wave-like shape. *C. kingii* uses this bipedal form of locomotion when fleeing or chasing after grasshoppers. Juvenile Frilled Lizards run on all fours (BEDFORD et al. 1993). From these authors we also know that Frilled Lizards prefer to live on bushes of the following species: *Eucalyptus tetrodonta*, *E. porrecta*, *E. miniata*, *Xanthostemum paradoxus*, *Livistona humilis*

70

and *Calytrix*. They particularly avoid using *Melaleuca sp., Pandanus spiralis* and *Euca-lyptus confertiflora* for climbing (SHINE & LAMBECK 1989). The latter named tree is one of the most common in the biotope of the Frilled Lizard in the Northern Territories. Unlike all other trees in the region it is rarely used by termites which are one of the most favoured prey of Frilled Lizards.

These authors fitted radio transmitters to three animals for a period of four months. These transmitters were able to locate the position of the lizards at any given time. It was found that the Frilled Lizards were rarely on the ground and when they were they almost invariably moved only on their hind legs, even when moving only very slowly. This was mainly to catch certain varieties of prey on the ground. Another reason was a small amount of interaction to other animals on the ground. It was never more than five minutes until they climbed onto a tree again. The radius of movement of males is three times as large as that of females. The former moved between 50 and 80 m per day within their habitat. The trees varied in height between 3 and 20 m. The animals remained at heights between 2 and 3 metres above the ground on these trees. However, most animals were seen at a height of around 10 m. *C. kingii* were not seen to indulge in any nocturnal activity. In the Australian summer Frilled Lizards are frequently encountered during the rainy season (December to April). WILSON & KNOWLES (1988) state that after a rain shower the lizards frequently descend from their elevated positions to move around on the ground. The reason for this is the hatching insects such as hymenoptera (wasps, bees and ants) and isoptera (termites) which the lizards catch and devour with great relish.

The lizards are only rarely seen during the dry season (May to August) (GRIFFITH & CHRISTIAN 1996). GREER (1989) was unable to explain the disappearance of these lizards at that time of year when temperatures of over 30°C are not uncommon. It has only recently been discovered that at this time of year Frilled Lizards conceal themselves amongst the leaves high in the trees and only rarely change their position (BEDFORD et al. 1993). The body and ambient temperature often rise to 40°C. In the Kakadu National Park, where SHINE & LAMBECK carried out their investigations, the annual rainfall is around 1,600 mm, most of which falls during the months of January to March. In July the highest temperature is 31°C and in October up to 39°C. Even when the lizards retreat into the shade their body temperature often still reaches 40°C. Their greatest problem therefore is not to obtain sufficient heat but rather to protect themselves from overheating. An arboreal lizard such as *C. kingii* barely has any other alternative to escape from the heat than to retreat into the shade of the leaves. To survive the shortage of food and water during the dry season Frilled Lizards are forced to alter their normal feeding habits and patterns of behaviour. Although the temperatures during the dry season are only slightly lower than those during the rainy season, the lizards reduce their body temperature out of all proportion by means of active thermoregulation (CHRISTIAN et al. 1996). By reducing their metabolic rate they save both energy and water. Further savings are made by limiting their movement and digestive activities and by limiting their social interaction (e.g., reproduction) to the more "bountiful" season. In this way they are also able to drastically reduce their weight loss per month although during the dry season they eat only half the volume of food that they eat during the rainy season. Constant metabolic rates during both the dry and rainy seasons resulted in a weight loss of 27% and caused death from starvation. However, due

Chlamydosaurus kingii   Photo: H.-D. Philippen

to the conservation measures mentioned above the actual weight loss was limited to only 1.3% (CHRISTIAN et al. 1996)! Thus body growth is naturally also limited to the rainy season.

It may sound something of a paradox but bush fires during the dry season also help to improve the food situation for Frilled Lizards (GRIFFITH & CHRISTIAN 1996a). Most animals survive the small fires at the beginning of the dry season by simply retreating to parts of the trees that the flames cannot reach, but larger bush fires towards the end of the dry season accounted for the demise of around 29% of the lizards in the area being investigated (GRIFFITH & CHRISTIAN 1996b). For those that survive the fires however, food be-

comes abundant in that the ground-covering vegetation has been removed and the prey is unable to find cover. Stomach analyses showed that in burned areas Frilled Lizards were able to catch considerably more insects than they could in areas which had not been burned. Larger prey animals are obviously easier to find. It is therefore no wonder that Frilled Lizards prefer "fire-cleared" areas and even actually colonise such regions (GRIFFITH & CHRISTIAN 1996a).

Food

The food spectrum of Frilled Lizards includes cicadas which they catch on trees. On the ground they eat numerous large insects and spiders. To investigate their food spectrum animals were earlier caught and dissected to allow an analysis of the stomach contents to be made. Nowadays however, it is usually only the stomach contents of preserved museum specimens that are analysed. Newly-caught live animals usually defecate soon after being caught or they are given an enema to allow examination of the faeces. SHINE & LAMBECK (1989) examined 124 live and museum specimens and found that butterfly caterpillars formed the predominant proportion of the contents of all stomachs (56% in all specimens examined). In addition there was also a large proportion of green ants (*Oecophylla smaragdina*), termites and beetles. The animals which we fitted with radio transmitters were usually found hunting for prey in the morning (around 0900 h) and afternoon (around 1700 h). They sat at a height of 2-3 m in the trees carefully watching the ground for suitable prey. Should something suitable come into view they reversed down the tree and ran on two legs in hot pursuit. Once they had caught-up with the prey they fell onto all fours to overpower it. As soon as the agama had eaten its prey it climbed into the next tree.

EHMANN (1992) states that ants are the most favoured food which Frilled Lizards, like *Moloch*, lick-up in vast numbers from ant paths and nests. It has been reported that they also take eggs from birds nests (GERLACH 1960). They will also eat small mammals should they come within striking distance. In captivity these lizards will take pieces of meat although they will not eat any plant material. Frilled Lizards are "sit-and-wait" hunters which watch very carefully for any suitable passing prey. This method of hunting is utilised by species which attack larger prey. If the prey is small (ants, beetles, termites) they are hunted actively. When one considers the most favoured food of a Frilled Lizard it is safe to assume that they must run-around. However, the exact opposite is true which

contradicts the findings of HUEY & PIANKA who determined that lizards which prefer small prey have to hunt many of them to satisfy their hunger. When one considers the size of the body of Frilled Lizard, its impressive jaw muscles and its predatory dentition one would not think this to be a lizard that prefers small prey. The so-called "small prey" is devoured by Frilled Lizards in hundreds or even thousands "at one sitting", particularly when the insects are hatching or swarming during the rainy season. Amongst monitor lizards there are similar examples, e.g., *Varanus rudicollis*, for a remarkable observation of the consumption of plant material see the chapter "Rearing the young".

Natural enemies

Many birds of prey, monitor lizards and giant snakes are potential predators upon Frilled Lizards. We have no detailed information. Aboriginals have hunted and eaten Frilled Lizards for many, many years. SCHRIRE (1982) proved this by means of bones found during excavations in Arnhem Land in the Northern Territories.

Reproduction in the wild

In the Northern Territories the breeding season of the Frilled Lizard begins before the rainy season and lasts from December until April. BEDFORD et al. (1993) were able to prove that *C. kingii* lays at least two clutches of eggs per season. These authors had nine female Frilled Lizards for examination. All were gravid and laid between 12 and 23 eggs per clutch. On the day of laying, the eggs in the smaller clutches weighed on average 2.7 g. The eggs in the largest clutch (23 eggs) weighed on average 4.4 g. BEDFORD et al. (1993) thus proved that the mass of eggs does not vary greatly within a clutch but rather between different clutches. At the end of these experiments three females were fitted with radio transmitters (after having laid eggs) and released into the wild. Using radar and bleepers they were located every 14 days, caught , x-rayed to determine whether they were gravid after which they were again released. Of the three females two were quickly gravid again for the second time in one breeding season The females were gravid for four to five weeks after which they laid their eggs. One of the "nests" was measured. It was 10-15 cm deep. The female buried ten eggs. The ground temperature where the eggs were laid was 28.8 - 33.7 °C. The morning average between 0900 and 1000 h was 29.5 °C, in the afternoon between 1600 and 1700 h around 31.9 °C. In the wild incubation took 69 days. On 24th January, 1993 all ten young hatched. Eight of them sat in a *Calytrix* bush only 1.5 m away from where the eggs had been laid. In comparison, adult lizards are never found in groups. Whether the forming of the young into "clubs" protects them from potential predators (BEDFORD et al. 1993) is open to discussion. They mention GREENE et al. (1978)

Chlamydosaurus kingii, a hatchling still inside the egg.   Photo: M. Schiberna

who assume such behaviour of *Iguana iguana*.

Under laboratory conditions the incubation of the eggs took 73 - 80 days at an average temperature of 30 °C. Young Frilled Lizards hatched after only 54 days in an incubator that had been kept at a constant temperature of 33 °C.

Captive husbandry
Vivarium type I
The first live Frilled Lizard to reach Europe was brought from Australia in 1893 and presented to an audience of scientists at a London museum by the naturalist Kent (BURTON et al. 1968). Until that date no vivarium observations had been published, the reason being that before 1900 only very few of these animals had been kept in zoos or private collections. They were usually aged individual specimens of which no-one took any particular notice. The belated breakthrough was achieved by Manfred REISINGER of Ergolding who managed to breed this species which he had described as "particularly difficult". The 1993 breeding statistics of the DGHT (German Herpetological Society) contain 26 *Chlamydosaurus kingii* juveniles which were bred by him. Other breeders have profited from this line and two years later achieved breeding successes themselves. During the intervening period (until October 1997) the number of Frilled Lizards kept in Germany has increased to 400 specimens. Legally imported Frilled Lizards from Indonesia are now available from both retail and wholesale sources. However, for the prospective purchaser there is always a certain element of risk since wild-caught animals are usually heavily infested with parasites (WEIS 1996). It is always better to buy captive-bred young. Details of good captive husbandry and breeding results can be found in REISINGER (1995). To house an adult pair of *C. kingii* we sug-

gest a large vivarium with the dimensions of a telephone call box: 130 × 100 × 220 cm (length × depth × height). Dimensions of this size will no doubt be off-putting for some interested parties and purchasers, but these minimum dimensions are absolutely essential. For such a relatively economical Frilled Lizard why such an expensive vivarium? Anyone in any doubt should first examine the vivaria in which the breeder houses his lizards and should then reconsider the decision to purchase animals of this species. Some keepers recommend that these lizards be housed singly and that they are only placed together for mating. The vivarium should contain stout climbing branches reaching from the floor to the roof, a drinking bowl and a 5 cm deep substrate consisting of coarse sand. Natural planting is superfluous because the lizards would destroy any growing plants in only a short time. Robust artificial plants are much better and will give an otherwise sterile vivarium a more attractive appearance. The vivarium should be lit by daylight fluorescent tubes (TLD series) and one or two spotlights or halogen lamps. A temperature of up to 38 °C is sufficient during the day and at night it should fall to room temperature. The vivarium should be thoroughly sprayed each morning before the lights are switched-on. These animals slough without any problems. Only when pieces of hard, old skin remain attached to the animals do they need to be removed from the vivarium and be bathed in tepid water to allow the old skin to be manually removed.

The aspect of how often these animals move should also be given careful consideration before the purchase because Frilled Lizards spend 90% of the day sitting motionless on a climbing branch. The only variation comes at feeding time when the animals react immediately and leave their resting place. In general they become quite tame and will eventually take food from the hand. Feeding these ani-

Chlamydosaurus kingii
Photo: H.-D. Philippen

mals too much or too frequently (to encourage the "statue" to move) will quickly lead to obesity in Frilled Lizards. Fat lizards re totally useless for breeding. We therefore suggest that the immobility be tolerated for three or four days before one instigates movement by introducing grasshoppers and beetles. It is possible to house this species with other lizards. HARCOURT (1986) keeps groups of *Egernia hosmeri* and *Chlamydosaurus kingii* together without any problems. The larger Frilled Lizards have never shown any aggression towards the much smaller Spiny Skinks. The same author reports that initially his Frilled Lizards would only drink water from the artificial plants after the vivarium had been sprayed. However, later they went-on to drink water from a bowl.

Captive breeding

To breed Frilled Lizards successfully it is advisable to hibernate them. Before hibernation the amount of food should be gradually re-

Chlamydosaurus kingii, a captive-bred juvenile.
Photo: H. Bosch

should take 10-14 days. If the animals have previously been housed separately it is at this time that they should be placed together.

During the subsequent mating the male bites the female firmly to ensure a good grip and to guarantee subsequent copulation. Females are gravid for four to six weeks after which they lay their eggs in fairly moist substrate (vermiculite or a mixture of sand and earth). HOSER (1989) measured several eggs. They were always around 28.5 mm long and 30 mm wide and always weighed around 5.3g. At an incubation temperature of 28.5 °C the young hatch after some three months. SCHIBERNA (pers. comm.) recommends an incubation temperature of 31 °C at which the young hatch after a maximum of 78 days. At lower temperatures the hatch rate was 70% and higher temperatures 100%. Incubation temperatures of around 31 °C correspond approximately to the field measurements recorded by BEDFORD et al. (1993).

Rearing the young

Hatchlings have a total length (TL) of between 13.5 and 16.5 cm. They eat only one day after hatching. We were informed by SCHUSTER of Rossdorf and SCHIBERNA of Stuttgart that their juvenile Frilled Lizards occasionally ate pieces of orange and kiwi fruit which were presented to them from forceps. This observation should be regarded as sensational because to date no Frilled Lizard has been known to take any vegetable matter (GREER 1989). Juveniles can normally be housed together for the first four months of life after which they begin to claim territories and bite one another. Stressed juveniles will not climb to elevated retreats. Instead they remain cowering on the ground. Separation usually helps spontaneously. IRWIN & IRWIN (1995) reported on a gravid female Frilled Lizard which was brought to Queensland Reptile

duced and then stopped completely. Before hibernation it is also wise to bathe the lizards in tepid water which encourages the animals to evacuate their digestive tract. During the winter the metabolic process does not stop completely, but it is reduced to a minimum. The temperature should be gradually reduced until finally both heating and lighting are switched-off. Further cooling is unnecessary. In our experience, a minimum temperature of 18-20 °C is quite adequate. After six to ten weeks the hibernation should be gradually ended. The waking and reactivation process and Fauna Park after an accident with a motor vehicle which it had barely survived. Unfortunately the lizard subsequently died. Of the ten eggs which had been removed from this female by caesarean section, two developed. The two young hatched independently but were very weak and had breathing problems. They were successfully ventilated but remained lethargic for several days and had to be force-fed. One of these young died after six months and the other thrived well.

Remarks

GREER (1989) describes the sudden popularity of the Frilled Lizard from 1982 to 1984.

Many Japanese tourists visited Australia because they wanted to see a Frilled Lizard either in a zoo or in the wild. Suddenly the Frilled Lizard was as popular and infamous as the koala or kangaroo. The main reason for this was the bluff of erecting the frill which caused great amazement in Japan. Another reason for this sudden fame was a television commercial for a motor car which featured a Frilled Lizard. Frilled Lizards became so popular with the Japanese that they would willingly pay one dollar for an Australian two-cent coin which depicts this lizard.

So do we! (The authors A. Hauschild & H. Bosch)   Photo: H.-D. Philippen

We like our
lizards frilled
NOT grilled

BUSH FIRES COUNCIL N.T.

Representation of *Chlamydosaurus kingii*
From long ago: A cave painting at Madjurnai,N.T.
From the present day: Aboriginal art after Lisa O'Mara

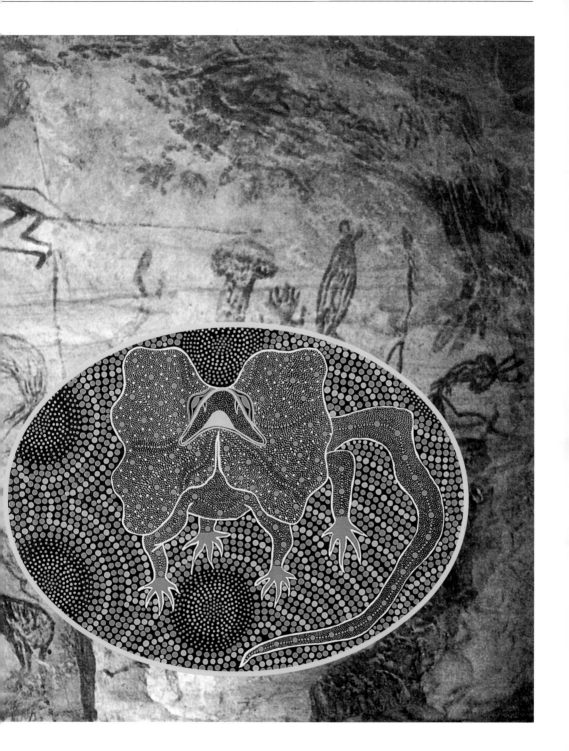

5. Diseases of Bearded Dragons and Frilled Lizards

Introduction

If incorrectly housed or fed in captivity Bearded Dragons and Frilled Lizards are susceptible to a multitude of infections (viral, bacteriological, mycotic or parasitic) and several non-infectious diseases. As has been reported of other lower invertebrates, under captive conditions the agamas are also subject to cold infections, a situation which has not been reported in animals in the wild and can therefore be categorically regarded as "captive artefacts" induced by incorrect housing or feeding conditions which must be evaluated as "artificially created". Each group of reptiles appears to have a very specific "susceptibility". Whilst amongst iguanas incorrect feeding often causes diseases of the skeleton or one of the many forms of gout, amongst agamas diseases caused by incorrect husbandry appear to dominate. Although externally Bearded Dragons and Frilled Lizards may have an extremely robust appearance, incorrect conditions such as temperature and humidity to which they are unaccustomed can have an extremely bad effect on them should they continue for a long period. They lie "motionless", often for some time, and then "suddenly" die "for no apparent reason" (as has often been reported)! As well as organ degeneration, the formation of tumors or various stages of gout, dissection often shows "only" trivial, secondary infections caused by a collapse of the body's immune system because of incorrect husbandry.

The most common infections of Bearded Dragons and Frilled Lizards under captive conditions are bacterial infections of immune suppressive animals. In chronically stressed agamas with a weakened immune system even ubiquitous, non-primary pathogenic causes (which under "normal" conditions would not cause illness) can quickly cause the symptoms of a generalised bacterial infection which infects more-or-less all the organs of the body. The main causes of death are inflammation of the lungs (pneumonia), the stomach and digestive tract (gastro-enteritis), the liver (hepatitis), the kidneys (nephritis) and the muscles of the heart or pericardium (myocarditis, pericarditis).

One of the most common and externally visible infections caused by "incorrect" husbandry of Bearded Dragons and Frilled Lizards is the formation of abscesses caused by all manner of bacteria, mainly mycosis (fungal infection) caused by a variety of pathogens. These are usually recognisable because of wet skin lesions which are usually very difficult to treat if the cause has not been determined beforehand. As inhabitants of habitats usually far away from water, Bearded Dragons and Frilled Lizards do not have as many parasites - even in their natural habitat - as other lizards which live close to water.

Amongst the Australian agamas being discussed here, both wild caught and captive-bred animals, the most predominant parasitic infections are the more-or-less harmless oxyures (threadworms or awltains) which are found in the rear section of the digestive tract. More rarely these lizards are hosts to the more dangerous ascarids (roundworms), rhabdiasids (lungworms), strongylids (bursa nematodes) or sprirurids ("curlytails") which if present in large concentrations can all cause death. Amongst lung parasites the most common in Bearded Dragons are pentasonids (tongue worms) which - as has already een seen - can infect an entire collection of aptive animals and in individual cases can lso cause the demise of the animal! Only very arely have cestodes (tapeworms) been found s parasites in the small intestine of these Australian agamas. Other forms of parasites rom the group of protazoa (unicellular parasites) and trematodes are mainly of academic nterest. As is the case when other reptiles are ept in vivaria, when Bearded Dragons and 'rilled Lizards are kept, these parasites are f relevance since if the animals are kept uner unhygienic conditions the parasites can nultiply at an alarming rate without an intermediate host being involved. This is particularly true of ectoparasites such as mites, but, s far as known, is only true for individual orms of internal parasites.

However, in comparison with other groups of izards, parasites in Bearded Dragons and 'rilled Lizards play only a subordinate role.

.1 Findings from the dissection of deceased Bearded Dragons and Frilled Lizards

ables 6 - 8 contain the dissection findings n 93 Bearded Dragons and 24 Frilled Lizrds. All dissected lizards had been kept in aptivity (zoos and private collections) and ere subjected to captive conditions for varyng lengths of time. They were dissected between 1966 and 1984 by Prof. Dr. W. Frank, Department of Parasitology, Zoological Instiute, Hehenheim University. The junior auhor assisted in the dissections. As far as we re aware this was numerically the most exensive survey of dissection findings of eearded Dragons and Frilled Lizards kept in aptivity. From this survey the clear "trends" f the frequency of diseases can be clearly een.

Table 6: Pathological and parasitic findings on 93 dissected Bearded Dragons
(36 wild-caught, 44 captive-bred, 13 not known)

Symptoms found	No. of agamas	%
Hepatitis/hepatosis	30	32
Pneumonia	26	28
Gout	20	21.5
Nephritis/nephrosis	17	18
Gastro-enteritis	16	17
Cachexy/marasmus	6	6
Trauma	6	6
Stomach overloading	5	5
Tumours	4	4
Heart muscle inflammation	2	2
Peritonitis	2	2
Egg binding/gravidity toxicosis	2	2
Coprostasis	1	1
Meningitis	1	1
Struma	1	1
Stress	1	1
No specific findings	9	10

Table 7: Infections found

Infections found	No. of agamas	%
1. Parasitoses		
Oxyures	25	27
Ascarids	1	1
Pentasomids	11	12
Cestodes	1	1
Amoebiasis	1	1
2. Generalised bacteria	17	18
3. (Skin) mycosis	6	6
4. Viruses	?	?

81

Findings on Bearded Dragons

Over 30% (!) of the 93 dissected Bearded Dragons showed pathological liver symptoms which ranged from liver inflammation to severe fatty degeneration of the liver ("fat liver"). With the exception of bacterial or parasitic liver infection diagnosed in only a few individual cases the severe fattening and degeneration of the liver was a result of inadequate husbandry conditions or incorrect feeding. Food insects and plants contaminated with insecticide may have played an important role. Almost 30% of the Bearded Dragons examined had various degrees of lung inflammation. As well as the frequent cases of bacterial pneumonia caused by unphysiological husbandry parameters an overproportional number of Bearded Dragons kept in zoological gardens died from parasitic pentasomiasis-pneumonia. Under favourable conditions these lung parasites can thus quickly reach epidemic proportions in a reptile collection.

When arranging and siting vivaria to house agamas care should be taken that no currents of cool air can flow to the heated agamas.

A further cause of predominantly dry pneumonia can be the dust from synthetic decorating materials (e.g., polyester, epoxy resins etc.). It is therefore vital that all such "artificial" decorating materials are carefully rinsed and dust-free before the agamas are installed in the vivaria.

Every fifth dissected agama (over 20%) was suffering from gout! This should be regarded as dramatic because this essentially metabolic disorder is unknown amongst captive animals that were wild-caught and its cause can only be evaluated as "incorrect captive husbandry". As well as pure gout of the kidneys the visceral form was also very common. In such cases the usually radiant white urates (salt of the uric acid) are deposited or stored on or in the organs of the bowels.

Because of the effects of the uric acid the infected organs or tissue may have garish white spots or speckling or may also appear to be infiltrated with white. Masses of uric acid several millimetres thick may also be stored or deposited in the pericardium or liver capsule thus preventing the normal function of the infected organic system and in dire cases causing the death of the animal. In severe cases of cardiac gout one frequently, and very appropriately speaks of "reinforced hearts". In these cases the heart muscle is "entombed" in the cardiac cavity which has become rigid because of the deposits of urate.

According to current knowledge it is not only gout of the kidneys, but also the various "stages" of visceral gout which are irreversible and thus cannot be cured. Too-dry husbandry conditions in combination with diet containing too much protein and insufficient ballast has been blamed for this severe metabolic disease. The prophylaxis of a gout is best guaranteed by having precise knowledge of the requirements of one's charges and their metabolic rate in captivity. The best prevention has proved to be regular spraying with tepid water each morning and evening to increase the atmospheric humidity in the vivaria which are frequently kept too dry. Bearded Dragons should also be given a regular supply of a variety of vegetable matter for fibre and roughage.

Acute kidney inflammations up to chronic nephropathies were found approximately as frequently as inflammations of the stomach, digestive tracts and general bacterial infections. In most cases the latter-named findings were typical debilitating infections caused as a result of incorrect husbandry. Insufficient food (death from hunger) and wasting as a result of old age accounted for the deaths of around 6% of the Bearded Dragons examined. Injuries from interspe ific fighting or fights with other species and raumatic collisions with furnishings which may be evaluated as "accidents" also accounted for the deaths of 6% of the animals examined.

Stomach overloading, usually as a result of ncorrect feeding or too opulent "force-feeding" accounted for the deaths of some 5% of he Bearded Dragons examined, a clear indication of incorrect husbandry of these reptiles.

Tumours, mainly in older animals were found in 4% of the Bearded Dragons. Other findings, e.g., inflammation of the abdomen, egg-binding (the so-called "gravity toxicosis"), constipation, inflammation of the meninges or the formation of goitres were "only" found in individual cases. After being dissected, in around 10 % of the animals examined, no particular findings were made despite careful inspection. It is possible that hese cases may simply be assigned to the heading "vivarium stress".

The proof of parasites in deceased vivarium reptiles "suffers" as a result of dosages of various antiparasitica prior to the demise of he animals. Of the 93 dead Bearded Dragons dissected the most dominant form of parasites found were clearly oxyures which were found in almost every third Bearded Dragon. In the case of agamas fed and digesting normally those inhabitants of the digestive tract which can usually be ignored only present potential danger when the hosts with a large number of oxyures are placed in hibernation. As has been found the oxyures do not rest and cannot be expelled by the host. It is therefore essential that before being allowed to hibernate the agamas should be treated for oxyures as a matter of routine. Regarding the high number of pentasomids found in these examinations it should be said that Bearded Dragons in their natural distribution range are hosts to their

"own", very sparsely distributed form of tongue worms which were only found in very isolated cases in the dissected animals. The specimens found in the dissected Bearded Dragons were mainly pentasomids which in the collections of several zoological gardens were rife and not host-specific and infected a large number of lizard hosts. This proves that Bearded Dragons are particularly suitable hosts for pentasomids.

The percentage (6%) of Bearded Dragons with fungal infections is also amazingly high. These ere obviously also the result of incorrect husbandry conditions which softened the skin barrier which under normal circumstances would be impenetrable to fungi.

The discussion of viral infections has only taken place during recent years. In the case of these two groups of Australian agamas these are still a matter of purely academic significance.

Findings amongst Frilled Lizards

The most obvious and grave findings amongst the 24 dissected Frilled Lizards (up to 1984) which had died under vivarium conditions (see Table 8) was the fact that 25% died as a result of egg-binding a form of the so-called "gravity toxicosis". This is clear proof that these attractive lizards were previously kept under unsuitable and incorrect conditions whereby females were obviously not provided with suitable places in which to lay their eggs. The high percentage (25%) of bacterial infections which can be evaluated as "debilitating diseases" together with the high number of stomach-digestive tract inflammations (21%) and incorrect feeding (21%) or lung inflammations (17%) are also a clear indication of incorrect captive husbandry conditions. Interestingly - as in case of Bearded Dragons - 21 % of the dissected Frilled Lizards also had a form of gout which

Table 8: Pathological findings on 24 dissected Frilled Lizards (wild-caught)

Pathological findings	No. of agamas	%
Egg binding/gravidity toxicosis	6	25
Bacterial infections	6	25
Gastro-enteritis	5	21
Cachexy/marasmus	5	21
Gout	5	21
Pneumonia	4	17
Trauma	3	12.5
Hepatitis/hepatosis	2	8
Heart muscle inflammation	2	8
Mycosis	1	4
Tumours	1	4
General organ degeneration	1	4
Peritonitis	1	4

in this case too was probably the result of vivarium condition which were too dry. At 21.5 the number of physical injuries was twice as high as those found in Bearded Dragons (6%). In comparison, the number of liver diseases was very low amongst Frilled Lizards. Only 8% had a pathological liver condition (as opposed to 31% in Bearded Dragons). Likewise, only 8% were found to have infections of the heart musculature. This could be attributed to these agamas being too highly stressed under vivarium conditions. All other findings were only in individual animals and may therefore be regarded as insignificant.

Comparison of the findings

From direct comparison of the findings in the two groups of agamas it can be clearly seen that Frilled Lizards react much more sensitively to incorrect and inadequate vivarium husbandry conditions than the "uncom-

plicated" Bearded Dragons. An example is that they are less willing to accept an oviposition site that is less than ideal. However, amongst Bearded Dragons, organ degeneration appears to be more widespread. Amongst Frilled Lizards (only under captive conditions?)

Parasitic infections do not appear to play a dominant role. This is possibly a consequence of their natural selection of food animals amongst which there are obviously fewer animals that act as intermediate hosts. Thus there remain only those parasites which develop directly.

5.2 Health problems in vivarium practice

Parasitic infestations

Amongst *Pogona* and *Chlamydosaurus* the most prominent parasitic infestations are oxyures. If one wishes to combat these the most effective means is by the use of Molevac TM (Parke-Davis) which the animals tolerate well and which should be given in a dosage of 1 ml kg/bw (body weight). One dosage is sufficient but this should be repeated before the animals are encouraged to go into hibernation.

Ascarids (roundworms) and other nematodes in the digestive tract react very quickly to fenbendazol (Panacur TM, Hoechst) at a dosage of 30 (to 50) mg kg/bw. In the case of ascarids this dosage should be repeated several times. Another effective means of combating infestations of threadworms is febantel (Rintal TM, Bayer) which in the case of nematodes infesting the digestive tract and lungs should be given in a dosage of 50 mg kg/bw daily for five to seven days. Pentasomids - like all other internal parasites as well as mites and tics - may be treated with ivermectin (Ivomec TM, Merck, Sharp & Dohme MSD). A minute dosage of only

).5 mg kg/bw is sufficient to kill-off these parasites. However, they remain in the lungs and in the case of a severe infestation their waste products may lead to the demise of the host animal.

As far as bacterial infections are concerned the husbandry conditions under which the Bearded Dragons and Frilled Lizards are kept should be critically examined. In many cases only minor modifications and improvements such as an increase in temperature or atmospheric humidity or the provision of natural light (unfiltered sunlight!) are sufficient to alleviate the problem. In severe cases a suitable means of treatment and a treatment programme must be formulated by a competent laboratory or institution. In recent years a number of publishers have produced a variety of books detailing new treatments and medications in table form. We recommend the following books in alphabetical order of the authors names: GABRISCH & ZWART (1987); ISENBÜGEL & FRANK (1985); KÖHLER (1996).

Egg-binding

Egg-binding usually occurs in wild-caught animals which are gravid when imported but also occasionally occurs in captive-bred animals. Several factors may prevent females from laying eggs. In most cases it is only stress which brings females into this life-threatening situation. An observant keeper will house such a female singly to prevent such a situation arising. Frequently an increased calcium discharge from the oviduct is also the cause. The normally smooth shell of the egg is then very rough. A further cause is a deficiency of vitamin A or vitamin E which reduces the slippiness of the mucous membranes in the uterus and prevents the eggs from entering the uterus (ISENBÜGEL & FRANK 1985). In general the female is in such poor condition she does not have the strength to go through the laying process. The veterinary surgeon should first take an x-ray to ensure that this is indeed the case. If the eggs are not too large to pass through the oviduct or cloaca the animal will then be given an injection of calcium. If this calcium substitute does not produce the desired effect a subsequent injection of oxytocin will be given. Oxytocin is a labour-inducing hormone. If several doses of this preparation do not produce the desired result the veterinary surgeon must perform a caesarean section to solve the problem. In most cases the female will survive this operation but must not be allowed to become gravid again to prevent any future operations being required.

Sloughing difficulties

Incomplete sloughs or metabolic disturbance can lead to sloughing difficulties: tail tips which do not slough completely will die-off. In such cases the keeper must intervene and "rub-off" any remaining pieces of skin. If this is difficult when the skin is dry, then the skin must be softened in a warm bath. If the animals has a disease of the skin it is advisable to ask the veterinary surgeon to administer an injection of a combination of vitamins A, D_3, E and C (ISENBÜGEL & FRANK 1985). In the opinion of SCHUSTER (Rossdorf) a deficiency of vitamin C can be one of the main causes of sloughing difficulties. SCHUSTER encourages his Bearded Dragons to eat pieces of orange or kiwi fruit occasionally and in his case this fruit cocktail serves to prevent sloughing difficulties.

Sloughing problems with the frill of Frilled Lizards

In captive husbandry it has been shown that the frill of Frilled Lizards, which is a simple skin duplication, is predestined for injury and infection especially within the limited confines of the vivarium. After sloughing problems or fights the frills are particularly "open" and thus very susceptible to fungal infections which if not treated can lead to large parts of the frill dying-off. Parts of the frill damaged in such a way will not regenerate and are lost forever.

Necrosis of the toes and tail
The dying-off or drying-out of the tip of the tail or toes can be frequently seen amongst juveniles. It is mainly juvenile Bearded Dragons which are affected but it may also occasionally occur in Frilled Lizards. The main cause is injury, e.g., by being caught in the vivarium door or sliding glass panel. It can also happen that the tail gets caught in the fork of a climbing branch or may be injured on a corner when being lashed from side to side. The bruising or crushing can damage blood vessels and thus reduce the circulation through the appropriate part of the tail. Thus the reduced supply of oxygen together with an increase in the toxic metabolic products causes necrosis, i.e., the dying-off of the tissue (KÖHLER 1996).
Remaining pieces of skin on the tail can lead to strangulation of the relevant part and can also cause that part of the tail to die-off. After each slough it is therefore vital to ensure that all old skin has been removed from the tail and toes.

Overgrown claws
Amongst Bearded Dragons it is often seen that their claws grow disproportionately long if the substrate upon which they are kept is too soft. If these agamas have no way to wear-down their claws naturally they grow too long and hinder the movements of the animal. This is obviously uncomfortable for the animal and means that the keeper must intervene to shorten the claws. When cutting the claws only the part which does not contain blood vessels should be removed. In most cases

however, it suffices to change the substrate. The best substrates have proved to be coarse sand or fine aquarium gravel.

Genetic defects
The intense captive husbandry and breeding of Bearded Dragons has allowed genetic defects to become something of a problem. In their standard work ISENBÜGEL & FRANK (1985) describe some genetically caused growth problems. From a clutch of young produced by a breeding pair of Pogona vitticeps 70 % of the young developed normally. The remainder had rails which curled to the side which cannot be done with normal animals. During their growth no further peculiarities were externally visible. On attaining sexual maturity these juveniles produced their first generation of young, of which, once again 30% had "curly tails". This generation of deformed Bearded Dragons also had deformed spines and quickly died from breathing difficulties because the deformed spinals column was pressing against the internal organs. In order to determine which parent was the carrier of the genetic defect, the male was paired with a known healthy female. The young from this pairing were externally normal. According to the junior author (BOSCH) the pairing of a known healthy male with the original female again produced young with "curly tails". SCHUSTER of Rossdorf also reported on a clutch of young Pogona henrylawsoni some of which also had "curly tails". Here again the female was the carrier of the genetic defect.

Cancers
At around ten years of age tumours occasionally begin to form in Bearded Dragons and Frilled Lizards. Could these be caused by old age? Unfortunately, to date no detailed studies have been carried out. In such a situation the only humane solution is to put the animal painlessly to sleep.

5. Protection and conservation measures

All Australian animals are now subject to extremely strict export regulations. However, because animals of the genus Pogona are now commonly bred in Germany and other European countries as well as in the United States and because of the fact that they breed so easily, there is now no need to resort to bringing animals from the wild and this has resulted in a dramatic reduction in the number of animals being smuggled out of Australia. Captive-bred young Bearded Dragons and Frilled Lizards can now be commonly bought from breeders and reptile dealers without any need for them to be registered.

Because protection and conservation measures vary widely from country to country, even within the European Union, the authors strongly advise that you make enquiries at your national Department of the Environment before obtaining animals of these genera. In a court of law, ignorance of regulations will not always be accepted as innocence! Care, forethought and advance enquiries are therefore the watchwords for anyone wishing to obtain animals of these genera.

Many herpetological societies around the world have published guidelines for the correct husbandry of these animals and general indications of the conditions needed for their well-being are contained in the following table. This table refers to the basic requirements of and adult pair of *P. vitticeps* with an average SVL of 25 cm. For such a pair the minimum vivarium dimensions should be:

Length: 125 cm
Depth: 100 cm
Height: 75 cm

For each additional animal the ground area should be increased by 15 %. These dimensions should also be adequate for *Chlamydosaurus kingii* which have also been successfully kept and bred under such conditions.

Table 9 – Requirements for the adequate housing of **Pogona**

Name	Habitat	Vivarium size for 1,1, (L×D×H) in SVL	Ground temp. °C	Basking place	Social composition life expectancy	Remarks
Bearded Dragon	dry/hot	5×4×3	25-30	50 °C	1, x (10)	Caves, branches, stacked rocks

7. Glossary and abbreviations

Technical terms not contained in this glossary are explained elsewhere in the text. Anyone wishing to delve more deeply should consult ULBER et al. (1989). "Dictionary of Herpetology" published by the Berlin Herpetological Society (176 pages) or PETERS J. A. (1964), "Dictionary of Herpetology" published by Hafner Publishing Company, New York and London (392 pages).

adaption: adaptation (in this case ecological)

adult: Sexually mature, fully-grown

arid: Dry. An arid climate is one in which the annual evaporation is greater than the annual rainfall

autotomy: The ability to discard body parts which eventually regenerate (e.g., in the case of many lizards, the tail)

biotope: The natural habitat of a plant or animal species

dorsal: On the back

habitat: The area where a species lives

hemipenis: Male sexual organ. Male snakes and lizards have paired sexual organs only one of which is inserted during mating

humid: Moist, an area of heavy rainfall

inc. sed.: incerta sedis - uncertain placement in the taxonomics

juvenile: Not yet sexually mature

kg/bw: per kilogram of body weight

lateral: On the side

monotypic: The only species of a genus

morphological: Concerning the build and shape

nomenclature: The allocation of scientific names

oviparous: Egg-laying

semiadult: The transition period from juvenile to sexually mature

SVL: Snout-vent length. The length from the tip of the snout to the cloacal opening

taxonomy: The description, naming and allocation to a system

thermoregulation: The control of optimum body temperature by cooling or heating

TL: Total length. The length from the tip of the snout to the tip of the tail.

TLL: Tail length. The length from the cloacal opening to the tip of the tail.

tympanum: Ear drum, ear opening

ventral: On the belly

viviparous: Giving birth to live young.

8. Appendix

Table 10 – Checklist of recent agamas

Genus	First described by	No. of species	Distribution
Acanthocercus	FITZINGER, 1843	8	Asia, Africa, Europe
Acanthosaura	GRAY, 1831	4	Asia
Agama	DAUDIN, 1802	32	Africa
Amphibolurus	WAGLER, 1830	3	Australia, New Guinea
Aphaniotis	PETERS, 1864	3	Asia
Brachysaura	BLYTH, 1856	1	Asia
Bronchocela	KAUP, 1827	7	Asia
Bufoniceps	ARNOLD, 1992	1	Asia
Caimanops	STORR, 1974	1	Australia
Calotes	CUVIER, 1817	20	Asia
Ceratophora	GRAY, 1834	5	Asia
Chelosania	GRAY, 1845	1	Australia
Chlamydosaurus	GRAY, 1825	1	Australia, New Guinea
Complicitus	MANTHEY, 1997	1	Asia
Cophotis	PETERS, 1861	1	Asia
Coryphophylax	FITZINGER, 1843	1	Asia
Cryptagama	WITTEN, 1984	1	Australia
Ctenophorus	FITZINGER, 1843	24	Australia
Dendragama	DORIA, 1988	1	Asia
Diporiphora	GRAY, 1842	15	Australia, New Guinea
Draco	LINNAEUS, 1758	21	Asia
Gonocephalus	KAUP, 1825	17	Asia
Harpesaurus	BOULENGER, 1885	5	Asia
Hydrosaurus	KAUP, 1827	3	Asia
Hypsilurus	PETERS, 1867	13	Mikronesien, Melanesien, New Guinea, Australia
Japalura	GRAY, 1853	24	Asia
Laudakia	GRAY, 1845	19	Asia
Leiolepis	CUVIER, 1829	7	Asia
Lophocalotes	GÜNTHER, 1872	1	Asia
Lophognathus	GRAY, 1842	4	Australia
Lyriocephalus	MERREM, 1820	1	Asia

Tabelle 10 – Checklist of recent agamas

Genus	First described by	No. of species	Distribution
Mictopholis	SMITH, 1835	1	Asia
Moloch	GRAY, 1841	1	Australia
Oriocalotes	GÜNTHER, 1864	1	Asia
Otocryptis	WAGLER, 1830	2	Asia
Paracalotes	BOURRET, 1939	1	Asia
Phoxophrys	HUBRECHT, 1881	5	Asia
Phrynocephalus	KAUP, 1825	38	Europe, Asia
Physignathus	CUVIER, 1829	2	Asia, Australia
Pogona	STORR, 1982	8	Australia
Psammophilus	FITZINGER, 1843	2	Asia
Pseudocalotes	FITZINGER, 1843	6	Asia
Pseudocophotis	MANTHEY, 1997	1	Asia
Pseudotrapelus	FITZINGER, 1843	1	Africa, Asia
Ptyctolaemus	PETERS, 1864	2	Asia
Salea	GRAY, 1845	4	Asia
Sitana	CUVIER, 1829	3	Asia
Thaumatorhynchus	PARKER, 1924	1	Asia
Trapelus	CUVIER, 1816	14	Europe, Africa, Asia
Tympanocryptis	PETERS, 1863	9	Australia
Uromastyx	MERREM, 1820	10	Africa, Asia
Xenagama	LOVERIDGE, 1942	2	Africa

(after MANTHEY & SCHUSTER (1999))

9. Bibliography

The entries marked with an asterisk * deal with the subject. Behind each entry we mention the species with which the article or book is concerned.

BADHAM, J. A. (1976): The *Amphibolurus barbatus* species-group (Lacertilia: Agamaidae).- Aust. J. Zool., **24** : 423-43. *P. barbata, P. vitticeps, P. minor, P. minima, P. microlepidota, P. nullarbor.*

BECH, R. & U. KADEN (1990): Vermehrung von Terrarientieren. Echsen.- Urania Verlag, Leipzig; Jena; Berlin, 168 S. *P. barbata.*

BEDFORD, G. S., K. A. CHRISTIAN & A. D. GRIFFITHS (1993): Preliminary investigations on the reproduction of the Frillneck Lizard *Chlamydosaurus kingii* in the Northern Territory.- In: LUNNEY, D. & AYERS, D. (Hrsg.): Herpetology in Australia.- Transactions of the Royal Zoological Society of New South Wales, 414 S. *C. kingii.*

BÖHME, W. (1981): Handbuch der Reptilien und Amphibien Europas. Bd. 1. Echsen (SAURIA) I.- Akademische Verlagsgesellschaft, Wiesbaden, 520 S.

BRATTSTROM, B. H. (1971): Social and thermoregulatory behavior of the Bearded Dragon, *Amphibolurus barbatus*.- COPEIA, **1971**: 484-497. *P. barbata.*

BROWNE-COOPER, R. (1984): Notes on the reproduction of the Bearded Dragon *Pogona minor*.- Herpetofauna, Sydney, **15** (1-2): 49. *P. minor.*

BURTON, M. & R. BURTON (1968): Encyclopedia of the Animal Kingdom.- BPC Publishing Ltd., London, 476 S. *C. kingii.*

BUSH, B. (1981): Reptiles of the Kalgoorlie-Esperance region.- Published by the author, Esperance, 48 S. *P. minor.*

– (1992): Some records of reproduction in captive lizards and snakes.- Herpetofauna, Sydney, **22** (1): 26-31. *P. minor.*

BUSH, B., B. MARYAN, R. BROWNE-COOPER & D. ROBINSON (1995): Guide to the Reptiles and Frogs of the Perth Region.- University of Western Australia Press, Nedlands, Australia, 211 S. *P. minor.*

BUSTARD, H. R. (1966): Notes on the eggs of *Amphibolurus barbatus vitticeps*.- Brit. J. Herp., London, **3**: 252-259. *P. vitticeps.*

– *(1970): Australian Lizards.- William Collins Pty. Ltd. Sydney, New South Wales, 162 S. *P. barbata, C. kingii.*

CARPENTER, C. C. & J. A. BADHAM (1970): Behavior patterns of three species of *Amphibolurus* (Agamidae).- COPEIA, 497-505. *P. barbata.*

CHRISTIAN, K. A., A. D. GRIFFITHS & G. S. BEDFORD (1996): Physiological ecology of frillneck lizards in a seasonal tropical enviroment.- Oecologia, **106** (1): 49-56. *C. kingii.*

COGGER, H. G. (1979): Reptiles and amphibians of Australia.- Reed Books Pty. Ltd., Chatswood, New South Wales; 608 S. *C. kingii, P. barbata, P. microlepidota, P. minima, P. minor, P. mitchelli, P. nullarbor, P. vitticeps.*

– (1986): Reptiles and amphibians of Australia.- Reed Books Pty. Ltd., Chatswood, New South Wales; 688 S. *C. kingii, P. barbata, P. microlepidota, P. minima, P. minor, P. mitchelli, P. nullarbor, P. vitticeps*

– (1992): Reptiles and amphibians of Australia.- Reed Books Pty. Ltd., Chatswood, New South Wales; 775 S. *C. kingii, P. barbata, P. microlepidota, P. minima, P. minor, P. mitchelli, P. nullarbor, P. vitticeps.*

DALE, F. D. (1973): Fourty Queensland Lizards.- Queensland Museum Publ., 64 S. *C. kingii. P. barbata.*

DAVEY, K. (1970): Australian lizards.- Landsdown Press Pty. Ltd. Melbourne, 111 S. *C. kingii, P. barbata.*

* DAVIDGE, C. (1979): A census of a community of small terrestrial vertebrates.- Australian Journal of Ecology, **4** (2): 165-170. *P. minor*

– (1980): Reproduction in the herpetofaunal community of a *Banksia* woodland near Perth, W. A..- Aust. J. Zool., **28**: 435-43. *P. minor.*

DELL, J. & A. CHAPMAN (1981): Reptiles and Frogs of East Yuna and Bindoo Hill Nature Reserves.- Rec. West. Aust. Mus. Suppl. (**13**): 95-105. *P. minor.*

91

DE VOSJOLI, P. (1996): Step by step vivarium design: a naturalistic vivarium for small Bearded Dragons.- The VIVARIUM, Escondido, **7** (6): 36-37. *P. barbata, P. vitticeps, P. henrylawsoni.*

DE VOSJOLI, P. & R. MAILLOUX (1993): The general care and maintenance of Bearded Dragons.- Advanced Vivarium Systems, Inc., Lakeside, 64 S. *P. barbata, P. henrylawsoni, P. microlepidota, P. minima, P. minor, P. mitchelli, P. nullarbor, P. vitticeps.*

– (1996a): Species and Morphs of Bearded Dragons Pogona in U. S. Herpetoculture.- The VIVARIUM, Escondido, **7** (6): 28-35. *P. barbata, P. vitticeps, P. henrylawsoni.*

– (1996b): A simple system for raising juvenile Bearded Dragons (*Pogona*) indoors.- The VIVARIUM, Escondido, **7** (6): 42-44. *P. vitticeps.*

EHMANN, H. (1992): Enceclopedia of Australian Animals. Reptiles.- Angus & Robertson, Pymble/ New South Wales, 495 S. *C. kingii, P. barbata, P. mitchelli, P. nullarbor, P. microlepidota, P. minor, P. minima, P. vitticeps, P. henrylawsoni .*

ESTES, R. & E. E. WILLIAMS (1984): Ontogenetic variation in the molarifiorm teeth of lizards.- J. Vert. Paleon. **4** (1): 96-107.

FELLMANN, F. (1991): Note de Terrariophilie: *Amphibolurus barbatus vitticeps* (Agama burbu d' Australie).- Bull. Soc. Herp. Fr. (1991) **58**: 51. *P. barbata.*

FITZGERALD, M. (1983): A note on water collection by the Bearded Dragon *Amphibolurus vitticeps.*- Herpetofauna, Sydney, **2** (14): 93. *P. vitticeps.*

*FOGEL, D. (1993): The Inland Bearded Dragon (*Pogona vitticeps*).- Vivarium, Lakeside, CA, 4 (5): 15-17. *P. vitticeps, P. barbata.*

GABRISCH, K. & P. ZWART (1987): Krankheiten der Heimtiere. - Schlütersche Verlagsanstalt, Hannover, 2. Aufl.: 412 S.

GASSNER, P. & A. HAUSCHILD (1997): Kosmopoliten, aber keine „Allerweltstiere": Skinke der Gattung *Eumeces* WIEGMANN, 1834. - Reptilia, Münster **2** (2): 43-48.

GERLACH, R. (1960): Salamandrische Welt.- Claassen Verlag GmbH, Hamburg, 264 S. *C. kingii, P. barbata.*

GREEN, H. W., G. M. BURGHARD, B. A. DUGAN & A. S. RAND (1978): Predation and the defensive behavior of green iguanas (Reptilia, Lacertilia, Iguanidae).- J. Herpetol., **12**: 169-176.

GREER, A. E. (1989): The Biology and Evolution of Australian Lizards.- Surrey Beatty & Sons Pty Ltd., Chipping Norton, New South Wales, 264 S. *C. kingii, P. barbata, P. henrylawsoni, P. microlepidota, P. minima, P. minor, P. mitchelli, P. nullarbor, P. vitticeps.*

GRIFFITHS, A. D. & K. A. CHRISTIAN (1996a): Die and habitat use of frillneck lizards in a seasona tropical enviroment.- Oecologia, **106** (1): 39-48 *C. kingii.*

– (1996b): The effects of fire on the frillneck lizard (*Chlamydosaurus kingii*) in northern Australia.- Aust. J. of Ecology, **21**: 386-398. *C. kingii.*

*GRIFFITHS, K. (1984): Reptiles and Frogs of Australia.- View Productions Pty. Ltd., Sydney New South Wales, 96 S.

– (1987): Reptiles of the Sydney Region.- Three Sisters Productions Pty. Ltd., Winmalee, 120 S. *P. barbata.*

HARCOURT, N. (1986): A review of the Frilled Lizard *Chlamydosaurus kingii* in captivity.- Thylacinus **11** (3): 100-104. *C. kingii.*

HARDY, C. J. & C. M. HARDY (1977): Tail regeneration and other observations of an agamid lizard.- Aust. J. Zool., **19** (2): 141-148. *Physignathus lesueurii.*

HAUSCHILD, A. & P. GASSNER (1994): Zur Kenntnis von *Egernia kingii*: Morphologie, Ökologie, Terrarienhaltung und Zucht der Inselform von der Houtman Abrolhos/ Westaustralien.- SALAMANDRA, **30** (3): 185-196. *P. minima.*

– (1995): Skinke im Terrarium.- Landbuch-Verlag, Hannover, 197 S.

*HEATWOLE, H. F. & J. TAYLOR (1987): Ecology of Reptiles.- Surrey Beatty & Sons, Sydney. Chipping Norton, 325 S.

HENDERSON, I, (1992): The Bearded dragon, *Pogona sp.*, and it´s maintenance and breeding in captivity.- Herptile, **17** (1): 39-46. *P. vitticeps.*

HENLE, K. (1993): Issues in Australian Herpetology: A view from abroad.- In: LUNNEY, D. & D. AYERS (Hrsg.): Herpetology in Australia.- Transactions of the Royal Zoological Society of New South Wales, 414 S.

– (1995): A brief review of the origin and use of 'stellio' in herpetology and a comment on the nomenclature and taxonomy of agamids of the genus *Agama* (sensu lato) (Squamata: Sauria: Agamidae).- HERPETOZOA, **8** (1/2): 3-9.

HENKEL, F.-W. (1980): Zwei Terrarianer reisen nach Australien.- DATZ **33**: 422-426. *P. barbata, C. kingii.*

HIELSCHER, M. (1989): Haltung und Nachzucht der australischen Zwergbartagame *Pogona minima.*- elaphe, Schönow, **11** (2): 20-24. *P. minima.*

HOSER, R. T. (1989): Australian reptiles and frogs.- Pierson & Co., Sydney, 238 S. *C. kingii, P. barbata, P. mitchelli, P. vitticeps.*

- (1996): Reptiles encountered collecting in the Pilbara-Australia.- Reptilian, **4** (2): 25-35. *P. henrylawsoni, P. mitchelli.*

HOUSTON, T. F. (1977): Dragon Lizards & Goannas of South Australia.- South Australian Museum Publ., 84 S. *P. barbata, P. minor, P. nullarbor, P. vitticeps.*

HUEY, R. B. & E. R. PIANKA (1981): Ecological consequences of foraging mode.- Ecology, Chicago, **62**: 991-999.

IRWIN, S. & T. IRWIN, (1995): Notes on early develeopment in a hatchling - assisted Frilled Lizard (*Chlamydosaurus kingii*).- Herpetofauna, Sydney, **25** (2): 60-61. *C. kingii.*

ISENBUGEL, E. & W. FRANK 1985): Heimtierkrankheiten.- Ulmer Verlag, Stuttgart: 402 S.

JAROFKE, D. & J. LANGE (1993): Tierärztliche Heimtierpraxis 3, Reptilien, Krankheiten und Haltung.- Verlag Paul Parey, Berlin, Hamburg: 188 S.

JENKINS, R. & R. BARTELL (1980): A field guide to reptiles of the Australian High Country.- Inkata Press Pty. Ltd. Melbourne, 278 S. *P. barbata,*

JES, H. (1987): Echsen als Terrarientiere.- Gräfe und Unzer, München, 72 S. *P. barbata.*

*JOHN, W. (1968): Zwei Australier: *Amphibolurus barbatus* und *Egernia cunninghami.*- Aqua. Terra., **21**: 185-186. *P. barbata.*

JOHNSTON, G. R. (1979): The eggs, incubation, and young of the Bearded Dragon *Amphibolurus vitticeps* Ahl 1926.- Herpetofauna, Sydney, **11** (1): 5-8. *P. vitticeps.*

KARBE, B., D. KARBE & M. NIEHAUS-OSTERLOH (1991): Bunte Terrarienwelt. Die beliebtesten Amphibien und Reptilien.- Tetra-Verlag, Melle, 160 S. *P. barbata.*

KÄSTLE, W. (1973): Vollbart mit Hebelmechanik. Verhalten und Pflege der Bartagame.- Aquarien-

magazin **7** (2): 58-61. *P. barbata,*

KENNERSON, K. J. & G. J. COCHRANE (1981): Avid appetit for dandelion blossoms *Taraxacum officinale* by a Western Bearded Dragon *Amphibolurus vitticeps* AHL.- Herpetofauna, Sydney, **12** (2): 34-35. *P. vitticeps.*

KINGHORN, J. R. (1931): Herpetological notes. No.2.- Rec. Aust. Mus., **18** (3): 85-91. *P. barbata.*

KLINGELHÖFFER, W. (1957): Terrarienkunde III: Echsen.- Kernen Verlag, Stuttgart, 264 S. *C. kingii, P. barbata*

KÖHLER, G. (1996): Krankheiten der Amphibien und Reptilien.- DATZ Bücherei, Ulmer Verlag, Stuttgart: 160 S.

– (1997): Inkubation von Reptilieneiern. - Herpeton-Verlag, Offenbach, 205 S.

*LEE, A. K. & J. A. BADHAM (1963): Body temperature, activity, and behavior of the agamid lizard, *Amphibolurus barbatus.*- COPEIA, **1963**: 387-394. *P. barbata.*

LÖFFLER, E. & R. GROTZ (1995): Wissenschaftliche Länderkunden; Bd. 40: Australien.- Wissenschaftliche Buchgesellschaft, Darmstadt, 422 S.

LOVERIDGE, A. (1934): Australian Reptiles in the Museum of Comparative Zoology, Cambridge, Massachusetts.- Bull. Mus. Comp. Zool. Harv., **77**: 243-383.

MANTHEY, U. & N. SCHUSTER (1999): Agamen.- Herpetologischer Fachverlag, Münster, 120 S. *P. barbata, P. henrylawsoni, P. microlepidota, P. minima, P. minor, P. mitchelli, P. nullarbor, P. vitticeps.*

MOODY, S. M. (1980): Phylogenetic and historical biogeographical relationship of the genera in the family Agamidae (Reptilia, Lacertilia).- Ph. D. Thesis, Univ. of Michigan, 373 S.

NEUGEBAUER, W. (1972): Geglückte Aufzucht von Bartagamen.- Aquar. u. Terrarien Zeitschrift, **25** (12): 424-426. *P. barbata.*

*NIETZKE, G. (1972): Die Terrarientiere, Bd.II.- Eugen Ulmer Verlag, Stuttgart, 300 S. *P. barbata.*

*PETERS, U. (1972): Agamen im mittleren Neusüdwales.- DATZ, **25** (9): 320-321. *P. barbata.*

– (1986): Wir stellen vor: Agamen aus Australien.- Das Aquarium, **9** (207): 489-495. *C. kingii, P. barbata,*

*PETHER, J. (1996): Bartagamen.- Reptilia, Münster, 1 (1): 14-16. *P. vitticeps, P. barbata, P. henrylaw-*

soni, P. minima.

PETZOLD, H.-G. (1982): Aufgaben und Probleme bei der Erforschung der Lebensäußerungen der Niederen Amnioten (Reptilien).- BINA Verlag für Biologie und Natur, Berlin, 313 S. *P. barbata.*

PFLUGMACHER, S. (1984): Haltung und Zucht der Australischen Bartagame.- SAURIA, Berlin, **6** (3): 9-11. *P. vitticeps.*

PICKWORTH, B. (1981): Observation of behaviour patterns displayed by a pair of Bearded Dragons, *Amphibolurus barbatus* CUVIER.- Herpetofauna, Sydney, **12** (2): 13-15. *P. barbata.*

*PORTER, R. (1991): Unusual basking behavior in captive bearded dragons (*Pogona barbata*).- Herpetofauna, Sydney, **21** (2): 31. *P. barbata.*

RANKIN, P. (1977): Burrow plugging in the Netted Dragon *Amphibolurus nuchalis* with reports on the occurence in three other Australian Agamids.- Herpetofauna, Sydney, **9** (1): 18-23. *P. barbata.*

REISINGER, M. (1992): *Chlamydosaurus kingii* GRAY 1825, Haltung und Nachzucht der Australischen Kragenechse.- SAURIA, Berlin, **14** (1): 21-23. *C. kingii.*

– (1995): Erfahrungen bei der Haltung und Vermehrung der Kragenechse *Chlamydosaurus kingi.*- elaphe, Rheinbach, **1995** (3): 16-20. *C. kingii.*

RYBAK, M. (1996): Vittikins Dragons.- The VIVARIUM, Escondido, **7** (6): 26. *P. henrylawsoni, P. vitticeps.*

SCHAFER, S. (1979): Beards and Blue-Tongues.- Zoonooz, **52** (4): 14. *P. barbata.*

SCHMIDA, G. E. (1968): Erlebnisse mit Bartagamen.- DATZ, **21** (7): 27-30. *P. barbata.*

SCHRIRE, C. (1982): The Alligator Rivers Region: prehistory and ecology in Western Arnhem Land.- *Terra Australis* 7, 1-277. *C. kingii.*

SHEA, G. (1995): The holotype and additional records of *Pogona henrylawsoni* WELLS & WELLINGTON, 1985.- Memoirs of the Queensland Museum 38 (2): 574. *P. henrylawsoni.*

SHINE, R. (1990): Function and evolution of the frill of the frillneck lizard, *Chlamydosaurus kingii* (Sauria: Agamidae).- Biol. J. Linn. Soc. **40**: 11-20. *C. kingii.*

– (1991): Australian Snakes. - Reed Books, Chatswood, NSW, 223 S.

SHINE, R. & R. LAMBECK (1989): Ecology of frillneck lizards, *Chlamydosaurus kingii* (Agamidae), in tropical Australia.- Aust. Wildl. Res. **16**: 491-500. *C. kingii*

*SIMPSON, K. N. G. (1973): Amphibians, reptiles and mammals of the Murray River Region between Mildura and Renmark, Australia.- Memoirs of the National Museum of Victoria, **34**: 275-279. *P. barbata.*

SMITH, L. A. (1976): The Reptiles of Barrow Island.- West. Aust. Nat., Perth, **13**: (6): 125-136. *P. minor.*

SMITH, J. & T. D. SCHWANER (1981): Notes on reproduction by captive *Amphibolurus nullarbor* (Sauria: Agamidae).- Trans. R. Soc. South Australia, **105**: 215-216. *P. nullarbor.*

*SNYDER, R. C. (1962): Adaptions for bipedal locomotion of lizards.- American Zoologist, **2**: 191-203. *Ctenophorus cristatus.*

SPRACKLAND, R. G. (1993): Giant Lizards.- T. F. H. Publ., Inc., Neptune City, N. Y., 288 S. *C. kingii, P. vitticeps.*

SPRENKELS, A. J. H. (1990): *Amphibolurus barbatus/Pogona vitticeps* (WAGLER 1830) (Australische Baardagame).- XENOPUS, Lacerta Werkgroep Midden- en West-Brabant, **4** (24): 111-116. *P. vitticeps.*

STETTLER, P. H. (1981): Handbuch der Terrarienkunde.- Franckh´sche Verlagshandlung, Stuttgart, 228 S. *P. barbata.*

STORR, G. M. (1965): The Physiography, Vegetation and Vertebrate Fauna of the Wallabi Group, Houtman Abrolhos.- J. Roy.Soc.West.Aust., **48**: 1-14. *P. minima.*

– (1982): Revision of the Bearded Dragons (Lacertilia: Agamidae) of Western Australia with notes on the Dismemberment of the genus *Amphibolurus.*- Rec. West. Aust. Mus., **10** (2): 199-214. *P. microlepidota, P. mitchelli, P. minor, P. minima, P. nullarbor.*

STORR, G. M., L. A. SMITH & R. E. JOHNSTONE (1983): Lizards of Western Australia. II. Dragons and monitors.- University Western Australia Press, Nedlands, Western Australia, 113 S. *P. microlepidota, P. minor, P. nullarbor, C. kingii.*

STÖSSL, T. (1993): *Pogona barbata* (CUVIER).- SAURIA, Suppl., Berlin, **15** (1-4): 257-260. *P. barbata.*

SWAN, G. (1990): A fieldguide to the snakes and lizards of New South Wales.- Three Sisters Prod. Pty. Ltd., Winmalee/NSW, 224 S. *P. barbata, P. vitticeps.*

– *(1995): A photographic guide to snakes & other reptiles of Australia.- New Holland Ltd., London et al., 144 S. *P. barbata, P. vitticeps, P. minor, C. kingii.*

SWANSON, S. (1976): Lizards of Australia.- Angus and Robertson Publishers. London, 160 S. *P. minima, P. vitticeps, C. kingii.*

SWITAK, K. H. (1996): Reptilien im Kakadu - Nationalpark.- DATZ, **49** (8): 524-530. *C. kingii.*

THROCKMORTON, G. S., J. DE BAVAY, W. CHAFFEY, B. MERROTSKY, S. NOSKE & R. NOSKE (1985): The mechanism of frill erection in the bearded dragon *Amphibolurus barbatus* with comments on the jacky lizard *A. muricatus* (Agamidae).- Journal of Morphology **183**: 285-292. *P. barbata.*

ULBER, T., W. GROSSMANN, J. BEUTELSCHIESS & C. BEUTELSCHIESS : Terraristisch/ Herpetologisches Fachwörterbuch.- Hrsg. von der Terrariengemeinschaft e. V., Berlin, 176 S.

VAN STEIJN, N. P. (1989): De verzorging en kweek van de Australische baardagame (*Pogona vitticeps*).- LACERTA, Leiden, **47** (5): 140-146. *P. vitticeps.*

VALENTIC, R. A. (1995): Further instances of nocturnal activity in agamids and varanids.- Herpetofauna, Sydney, **25** (1): 49-50.- *P. vitticeps.*

WEIS, P. R. (1996): Husbandary and breeding of the Frilled Lizard (*Chlamydosaurus kingii*).- Pp. 87-92. In: P. D. STRIMPLE (ed.), Advances in herpetoculture. Special publications of the Herpetological Symposium, Inc. Number 1. Crown Craft Printing, Des Moines, 167 S. *C. kingii.*

WELLS, R. W. & C. R. WELLINGTON (1983): A synopsis of the Class Reptilia in Australia.- Aust. J. Herp.Suppl., **1** (3-4): 73-129. *P. barbata, P. microlepidota, P. minima, P. minor, P. mitchelli, P. nullarbor, P. vitticeps.*

– (1985): A classification of the Amphibia and Reptilia of Australia.- Aust. J. Herp. Suppl. , **1**: 1-61. *P. barbata, P. henrylawsoni, P. microlepidota, P. minima, P. minor, P. mitchelli, P. nullarbor, P. vitticeps.*

WERMUTH, H. (1959): Die Kragenechse, *Chlamydosaurus kingii* GRAY.- Aquarien und Terrarien, Leipzig, **6** (4): 108. *C. kingii.*

WERNING, H. (1995): Wasseragamen. - Herpetologischer Fachverlag, Münster, 96 S.

WILSON, S. K. & D. G. KNOWLES (1988): Australia's Reptiles.- William Collins Pty. Ltd. Sydney/ New South Wales, 477 S. *C. kingii, P. barbata, P. microlepidota, P. minor, P. nullarbor, P. vitticeps.*

*WITTEN, G. J. (1985): Relative growth in Australian agamid lizards: adaptation and evolution.- Aust. J. Zool. **33**: 349-362. *P. barbata, P. vitticeps, C. kingii.*

– (1994a): Taxonomy of Pogona (Reptilia: Lacertilia: Agamidae).- Memoirs of the Queensland Museum **37** (1): 329-343. *P. barbata, P. brevis, P. microlepidota, P. minor, P. minima, P. nullarbor, P. vitticeps.*

– (1994b): Relative growth in *Pogona* (Reptilia: Lacertilia: Agamidae).- Memoirs of the Queensland Museum, **37** (1): 345-356. *P. henrylawsoni, P. minor, P. minima, P. vitticeps.*

WITTEN, G. J. & A. J. COVENTRY (1990): Small *Pogona vitticeps* (Reptilia: Agamidae) from the Big Desert, Victoria, with notes on other *Pogona* populations.- Proceedings of the Royal Society of Victoria, **102**: 117-120. *P. barbata, P. vitticeps*

*WORRELL, E. (1963): Reptiles of Australia.- Angus and Robertson, Sydney, 207 S.

ZIMMERMANN, E. (1980): Durch Nachzucht erhalten: Bartagamen.- Aquarien Magazin, **14**: 86-94. *P. vitticeps*

– (1983): Das Züchten von Terrarientieren: Pflege, Verhalten, Fortpflanzung.- Frankh'sche Verlagsbuchhandlung, Stuttgart, 238 S. *P. vitticeps.*

*ZIMMERMANN, H. (1974): Letzte Rettung: der Kaiserschnitt. Zeitung und Geburt der Bartagamen - *Amphibolurus barbatus*.- Aquarien Magazin, **8**: 451-454. *P. vitticeps.*

ZWINENBERG, A. J. (1977a): Die Bartagame (*Amphibolurus barbatus*).- Aquaria 24 (9): 157-164. *P. barbata.*

– (1977b): The Bearded Dragon.- Bulletin Chicago Herpetological Society, **12** (4): 93-98. *P. barbata.*

Distribution:

Matthias Schmidt Publications
An der Kleimannbrücke 39
D-48157 Münster
Germany

Tel.: 0049-251-3270503
Fax: 0049-251-143955

E-mail: msp@ms-verlag.de
Home: www.ms-verlag.de